GCSE Success

Workbook

Science Higher

Brian Arnold • Elaine Gill • Emma Poole

Contents

Biology

Revised

A balanced diet and nutrition ... 4
The nervous system ... 6
The eye ... 8
The brain ... 10
Causes of disease ... 12
Defence against disease ... 14
Drugs ... 16
Hormones and diabetes ... 18
The menstrual cycle ... 20
Genetics and variation ... 22
Genetics ... 24
Inherited diseases ... 26
Selective breeding ... 28
Pyramids ... 30
Evolution ... 32
Adaptation and competition ... 34
Environmental damage 1 ... 36
Environmental damage 2 ... 38
Ecology and classification ... 40

Chemistry

Revised

Limestone ... 42
Fuels ... 44
Organic families ... 46
Vegetable oils ... 48
Plastics ... 50
Ethanol ... 52
Evolution of the atmosphere ... 54
Pollution of the atmosphere ... 56
Pollution of the environment ... 58

Revised

Evidence for plate tectonics ... 60
Consequences of plate tectonics ... 62
Extraction of iron ... 64
Iron and steel ... 66
Aluminium ... 68
Titanium ... 70
Copper ... 72
Transition metals ... 74
Noble gases ... 76
Chemical tests ... 78

Physics

Revised

Energy ... 80
Generating electricity ... 82
Renewable sources of energy ... 84
Heat transfer – conduction ... 86
Heat transfer – convection ... 88
Heat transfer – radiation ... 90
Heat transfer – warming, cooling, melting and boiling ... 92
Current, charge and resistance ... 94
Electrical power ... 96
Motors and generators ... 98
Domestic electricity ... 100
Waves ... 102
The electromagnetic spectrum ... 104
Analogue and digital signals ... 106
Nuclear radiation ... 108
Uses of radioactivity ... 110
The Earth in space ... 112
Stars and the universe ... 114
Exploring space ... 116

Notes ... 118

A balanced diet and nutrition

A

1 **Which carbohydrate is found in milk?** (1 mark)

a) glucose ☐
b) lactose ☐
c) maltose ☐
d) starch ☐

2 **A diet deficient in protein can lead to the disease** (1 mark)

a) influenza ☐
b) kwashiorkor ☐
c) measles ☐
d) pneumonia ☐

3 **Cholesterol is a type of** (1 mark)

a) carbohydrate ☐
b) fat ☐
c) protein ☐
d) vitamin ☐

4 **Which substance helps prevent constipation?** (1 mark)

a) fibre ☐
b) minerals ☐
c) vitamins ☐
d) water ☐

5 **What percentage of our body weight is water?** (1 mark)

a) 55% ☐
b) 65% ☐
c) 75% ☐
d) 85% ☐

B

1 **Complete the table by filling in the empty boxes.** (5 marks)

Nutrient	Found in	Used for
carbohydrate	cereals	
fibre		moving food in gut
	all food and drink	cools us down
protein	lean meat	
salt		nervous impulses

2 a) **The Atkins diet is a slimming diet which suggests that eating a lot of protein helps you to lose weight.**

How is the Atkins diet thought to work? (2 marks)

....

....

b) **What problems have been associated with the Atkins diet?** (2 marks)

....

C

1 Food manufacturers are required to label their products with nutritional information.

Look at the two labels and answer the questions.

Brendan's Beans

Typical values	per 100g
Energy	400kJ
Protein	7.0g
Carbohydrate	20.0g
Fats	1.0g
of which saturated	0.5g
Fibre	6.5g
Salt	1.0g

TOM's TOMATOES

Typical values	per 100g
Energy	70kJ
Protein	1.0g
Carbohydrate	3.0g
Fats	0.1g
of which saturated	trace
Fibre	0.5g
Salt	trace

a) How much energy per 100 g, do you get from Brendan's beans? (1 mark)

....

....

b) Explain which food is better for those trying to lose weight? (2 marks)

....

....

....

c) Which food is better for a person suffering from risk of strokes and why? (2 marks)

....

....

d) Brendan's beans contain more energy.

Explain one other reason why they are better for a teenager. (1 mark)

....

....

....

2 The table shows the energy needs of females of at different times in her life.

Life stage	Energy needs in a day in kJ
at infant school	8.500
at secondary school	9.500
adult	10.00
pregnant adult	11.500

a) Calculate the difference in her energy needs at infant and secondary school (2 marks)

....

....

b) Her activity is similar so why is there a difference. (1 mark)

....

c) Why does a pregnant female need more energy than a non pregnant one? (1 mark)

....

....

d) What happens to energy rich foods that are not used during respiration? (2 marks)

....

....

e) Name the disease commonly called 'the slimming disease'. (1 mark)

....

f) List two symptoms of the disease named in e. (2 marks)

....

How well did you do? 0-11 Try again 12-17 Getting there 18-23 Good work 24-29 Excellent!

The nervous system

A

1 The central nervous system (CNS) consists of (1 mark)

a) brain and the effectors ☐
b) brain and spinal cord ☐
c) spinal cord and receptors ☐
d) receptors and effectors ☐

2 Which structure is a sensory receptor? (1 mark)

a) liver ☐
b) kidney ☐
c) skin ☐
d) stomach ☐

3 Nerve cells are called (1 mark)

a) capillaries ☐
b) effectors ☐
c) neurones ☐
d) receptors ☐

4 Reflex actions help animals to (1 mark)

a) excrete ☐
b) grow ☐
c) reproduce ☐
d) survive ☐

5 The fatty sheath around a nerve cell is for (1 mark)

a) food ☐
b) insulation ☐
c) releasing a chemical ☐
d) slowing down conduction ☐

B

1 Complete the table by filling in the empty boxes. (5 marks)

Stimulus	Sense	Sense organ
	sight	eye
chemicals		taste buds (tongue)
sound waves	hearing	
pressure/temperature	touch	
	smell	nose

2 Complete the following passage. Use word from this list. (6 marks)

conscious involuntary learned reflex talking voluntary

The actions you think about are called .... actions. They are under .... control. They have to be .... e.g. ....
Actions that are automatic are called .... or .... actions.

C

1 **a) How is a nerve cell different to a typical animal cell?** (1 mark)

....

....

b) Explain how information is passed from one nerve cell to another. (4 marks)

....

....

....

....

....

....

2 **The passage of a nerve impulse always follows a set sequence of events. Use these words and phrases to show this sequence in the example given by filling in the boxes.** (7 marks)

effector
receptor
response
stimulus
motor neurone
relay neurone
sensory neurone

you sit on a drawing pin	
pain sensor in skin detects this	
nerve impulse sent to CNS	
nerve impulse transmitted in CNS	
nerve impulse sent to effector	
muscles contract	
you jump up	

3 **a) A reflex response to a new situation can be learned. What is this called?** (1 mark)

....

....

....

b) Explain how Pavlov demonstrated this. (3 marks)

....

....

....

....

....

....

....

....

....

....

The eye

A

1 Binocular vision means (1 mark)

a) one eye ☐
b) one eye on each side ☐
c) two eyes facing forward ☐
d) two eyes facing backward ☐

2 Which two structures produce an image on the retina? (1 mark)

a) conjunctiva and pupil ☐
b) cornea and lens ☐
c) iris and optic nerve ☐
d) sclera and brain ☐

3 Which defect is inherited? (1 mark)

a) blindness ☐
b) red-green colour blindness ☐
c) long sight ☐
d) cateracts ☐

4 In red-green colour blindness, which cells do not function correctly? (1 mark)

a) blood ☐
b) cones ☐
c) nerve ☐
d) rods ☐

5 In dim light, the pupil (1 mark)

a) closes ☐
b) gets bigger ☐
c) gets smaller ☐
d) stays the same ☐

B

1 Draw straight lines from the part of the eye to its description. (7 marks)

cornea	helps focus the image
lens	a hole that allows light through (in front of the lens)
muscular iris	the protective, white outer layer of the eye
optic nerve	contains light sensitive cells
pupil	controls how much light enters the eye
retina	transparent window in the front of the eye
sclera	receives nerve impulses from the retina and sends them to the brain

2 True or false? (3 marks)

	true	false
a) Predators usually have monocular vision.	☐	☐
b) Suspensory ligaments hold the lens in place	☐	☐
c) The eye is a sense organ	☐	☐

C

1 a) The diagrams shows an eyeball and light rays from an object.

Name the structures labeled A, B and C. **(3 marks)**

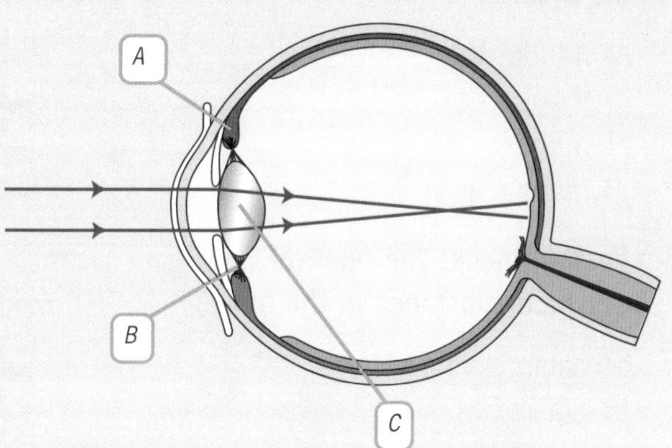

b) What defect does this eyeball show? Explain your answer. **(2 marks)**

....

....

....

....

c) Complete the table to show what happens to the structures when focussing on near and far objects. **(4 marks)**

Structure	Focussing on near objects	Focussing on far objects
ciliary muscles		
suspensory ligament		pulled tight
lens	fatter and rounder	

2 a) The sentences describe how the eye sees things but they are in the wrong order.

Fill in the boxes below to show the right order. **(4 marks)**

A The receptor cells in the retina send impulses to the brain.
B Light from an object enters the eye through the cornea.
C The brain interprets the image and you see the object the right way up.
D The curved cornea and lens produce an image on the retina.
E The image is upside down.

3 Complete the sentences using words from the list. **(3 marks)**

circular radial smaller

When a person moves from dim light into bright light, the iris reacts.

The .... muscles contract, the .... muscles relax.

The pupil gets .... Less light enters the eye.

The brain

A

1 **What is the storage and retrieval of information called?** (1 mark)

a) coordination ☐
b) memory ☐
c) perception ☐
d) transmission ☐

2 **Ecstasy affects the transmission of impulses across the** (1 mark)

a) cortex ☐
b) neurones ☐
c) medulla ☐
d) synapse ☐

3 **Which disease has no cure?** (1 mark)

a) epilepsy ☐
b) grand mal ☐
c) meningitis ☐
d) petit mal ☐

4 **How many neurones are there in the brain?** (1 mark)

a) hundreds ☐
b) thousands ☐
c) millions ☐
d) billions ☐

5 **Ecstasy blocks the removal of which substance in the brain?** (1 mark)

a) haemoglobin ☐
b) plasma ☐
c) melanin ☐
d) serotonin ☐

B

1 **The brain can suffer from many disorders.**

a) Describe the symptoms of petit mal seizures. (1 mark)

....

b) How are grand mal seizures different to petit mal seizures? (1 mark)

....

c) Complete the table by filling in the empty boxes. (6 marks)

Disorder	Possible causes/increases risk	Symptoms/facts
strokes		
Parkinson's		
tumours		

C

1 **a) The diagram shows a brain and the top of the spinal cord. Name the parts labelled A, B, C, D and E.** (5 marks)

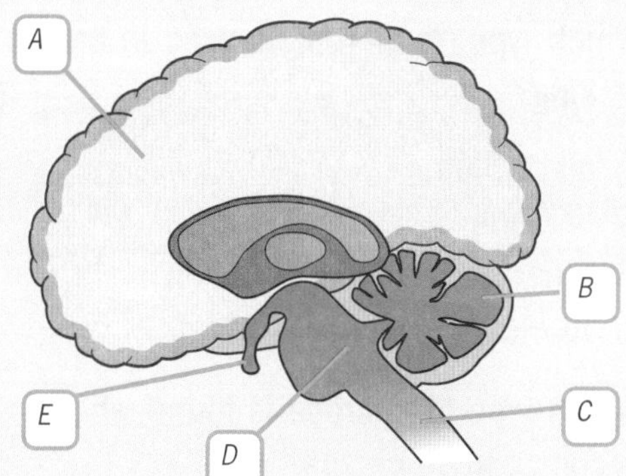

A ....

B ....

C ....

D ....

E ....

b) When you ride on a skateboard, different parts of your brain are responsible for different functions. Riding a skateboard is a complex activity. Many parts of the brain help to achieve this task.

Complete the table by filling in the letter (A, B, C, D, or E) (2 marks)

Function	Part of brain
controlling balance	
controlling heart and breathing rates	

c) On this diagram of the cerebral cortex, add labelling lines to show the areas that control the sensory areas, the motor areas, the memory and association areas. (3 marks)

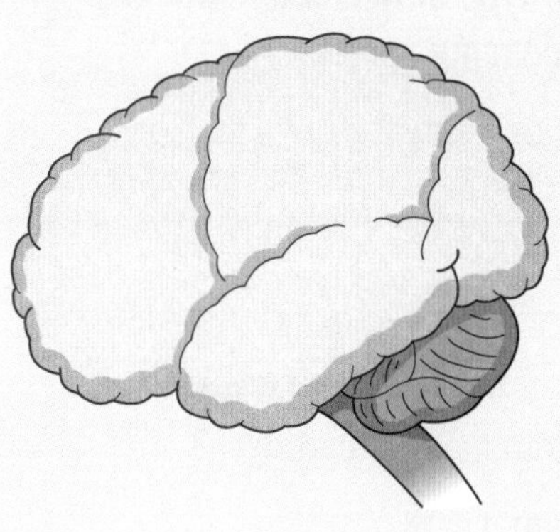

d) Write down two other facts about the cerebral cortex (2 marks)

....

....

....

....

2 **Explain the difference between short and long term memory.** (2 marks)

....

....

....

....

....

....

....

How well did you do? 0-10 Try again 11-16 Getting there 17-21 Good work 22-27 Excellent!

Causes of disease

A

1 Which type of microbe reproduces by producing spores? (1 mark)

a) all of them ❑
b) bacteria ❑
c) fungi ❑
d) viruses ❑

2 What is the name of an organism that transports a pathogen? (1 mark)

a) animal ❑
b) messenger ❑
c) plant ❑
d) vector ❑

3 Which disease is caused by a virus? (1 mark)

a) common cold ❑
b) food poisoning ❑
c) whooping cough ❑
d) ringworm ❑

4 Which type of microbe is used in bread making? (1 mark)

a) all of them ❑
b) bacteria ❑
c) fungi ❑
d) viruses ❑

5 Which type of microbe is found when decomposition occurs? (1 mark)

a) all of them ❑
b) insects ❑
c) fungi ❑
d) viruses ❑

B

1 The table shows features of bacteria and viruses.
Place a tick (if feature present) or a cross (if feature absent) in each box. (4 marks)

Feature	Bacteria	Viruses
cell wall		
protein coat		
respire, feed and move		
reproduce inside living cells		

2 a) List three symptoms of infection. (3 marks)

....

b) What name is given to microbes that get inside you and make you feel ill? (1 mark)

....

3 What is the difference between a benign and a malignant tumour? (2 marks)

....

C

1 a) Tuberculosis destroys lung tissue.

How is it spread? (2 marks)

....

....

....

....

b) List three things that helped to reduce tuberculosis. (3 marks)

....

....

....

....

....

....

2 Some diseases are not caused by microbes. Complete the table to show what causes the diseases listed. (4 marks)

Disease	Cause
anaemia	
cancer	
red-green colour blindness	
scurvy	

3 Write about three ways in which microbes can enter the body.

For each give an example of a disease spread in this way. (6 marks)

....

....

....

....

....

....

....

....

....

4 a) What happens to the cells in a cancer? (1 mark)

....

b) What is a mass of cancer cells called? (1 mark)

....

c) What is the most common cancer in men? (1 mark)

....

d) How can men reduce the risk of getting this cancer? (2 marks)

....

....

How well did you do? ✗ 0-14 Try again 15-21 Getting there 22-28 Good work 29-35 Excellent! ✓

Defence against disease

A

1 Which organ produces acid to kill bacteria? (1 mark)

a) heart ☐
b) liver ☐
c) kidney ☐
d) stomach ☐

2 Which is the resistant bacterium found in hospitals? (1 mark)

a) AIDS ☐
b) HIV ☐
c) MRSA ☐
d) STD ☐

3 Lymphocytes produce chemicals called (1 mark)

a) antibiotics ☐
b) antibodies ☐
c) antigens ☐
d) antiseptics ☐

4 What do antibodies do to the antigens? (1 mark)

a) kill them ☐
b) clump them together ☐
c) spread them out ☐
d) stop them moving ☐

5 In the MMR vaccine, R stands for (1 mark)

a) german measles/rubella ☐
b) measles ☐
c) meningitis ☐
d) rabies ☐

B

1 a) Antibiotics are used to kill bacteria inside the body.

Which microbe cannot be killed by antibiotics? (1 mark)

....

b) Why do scientists have to find new antibiotics to kill bacteria? (2 marks)

....

....

2 Complete the passage using words from the list. (4 marks)

antitoxins lymphocytes phagocytes white blood cells antibodies

If microbes get into your body, ... travelling around in your blood spring into action. White blood cells can make chemicals called .... that destroy the toxins produced by bacteria. White blood cells called .... produce .... which are like a tagging system labelling the microbes to be destroyed. The .... then come along and engulf these microbes destroying them. Antibodies stay in the blood for years.

C

1 a) Explain how your skin prevents microbes from entering your body. (3 marks)

b) When you cut yourself, microbes could get into your blood.

How does the blood kill microbes? (2 marks)

2 a) If you come into contact with a person suffering from mumps, the microbes could enter your body. Explain how you will develop a natural immunity to mumps. (5 marks)

b) Immunity can be also be artificial.

How is active artificial immunity different to natural immunity? (2 marks)

c) How is passive artificial immunity different to active artificial immunity? (1 mark)

3 a) Explain why new vaccines are needed against flu? (1 mark)

b) Explain why new vaccines are needed against HIV? (1 mark)

4 Drugs are tested before they are used to treat people. Explain why they might be tested on:

- healthy humans
- diseased humans (2 marks)

5 Which vaccine is controversial and why? (1 mark)

How well did you do? ✗ 0-12 Try again 13-18 Getting there 19-24 Good work 25-30 Excellent! ✓

Drugs

A

1 Which drug has recently had its classification changed? (1 mark)

a) cannabis ❑
b) cocaine ❑
c) heroin ❑
d) paracetamol ❑

2 Which drug makes you see and hear things that do not exist? (1 mark)

a) depressants ❑
b) hallucinogens ❑
c) pain killers ❑
d) stimulants ❑

3 Which drug is not a hallucinogenic drug? (1 mark)

a) cannabis ❑
b) cocaine ❑
c) ecstasy ❑
d) LSD ❑

4 What is the drug thalidomide now used to treat? (1 mark)

a) leprosy ❑
b) morning sickness ❑
c) common cold ❑
d) chickenpox ❑

5 Which drugs slow down the nervous system? (1 mark)

a) stimulants ❑
b) sedatives ❑
c) painkillers ❑
d) placebo ❑

B

1 Complete the sentences.

Use words from this list. (5 marks)

behaviour brain chemicals nervous system useful

Drugs are powerful ....; they alter the way the body works, often without you realising it. There are .... drugs such as antibiotics like penicillin, but these can be dangerous if misused. Drugs affect the .... and .... , which in turn affects .... and risk of infection.

2 True or false? (3 marks)

	true	false
a) alcohol increases the activity of the brain	❑	❑
b) alcohol is a depressant	❑	❑
c) alcohol can cause cirrhosis of the liver	❑	❑

C

1 The information is about birth weights of babies.

Mother	Average birth weight in kgs
non-smoker	3.50
smoker	2.90

a) How does smoking affect the birth weight of babies? (1 mark)

....

....

b) Explain how smoking causes this effect (2 marks)

....

....

....

....

....

2 Complete the table by filing in the organs each drug affects (6 marks)

Drug	Organs
alcohol	1....................................... 2.......................................
solvents	1....................................... 2....................................... 3.......................................
painkillers	1.......................................

3 Emphysema makes breathing difficult. Explain why. (2 marks)

....

....

....

....

4 a) What is the addictive substance in cigarette smoke? (1 mark)

....

....

b) Name the two other harmful chemicals in cigarette smoke and explain why they are harmful. (4 marks)

....

....

....

....

....

....

5 How do hallucinogens affect the body? (3 marks)

....

....

....

....

....

....

How well did you do? 0-12 Try again 13-19 Getting there 20-25 Good work 26-32 Excellent!

Hormones and diabetes

A

1 **Some diabetics can control the disease by a diet low in** (1 mark)

a) fat ❑
b) glucose ❑
c) protein ❑
d) starch ❑

2 **Which scientists discovered insulin?** (1 mark)

a) Banting and Best ❑
b) Jenner ❑
c) Darwin ❑
d) Watson and Crick ❑

3 **Which poisonous substance is completely removed from the blood by the kidneys?** (1 mark)

a) carbon dioxide ❑
b) salts ❑
c) urea ❑
d) water ❑

4 **Which gland produces insulin?** (1 mark)

a) adrenal ❑
b) thyroid ❑
c) pancreas ❑
d) ovary ❑

5 **Which is a symptom of diabetes?** (1 mark)

a) breathlessness ❑
b) cold ❑
c) hot ❑
d) thirst ❑

B

1 **Complete the sentences using words from the list.** (4 marks)

Diabetes   endocrine   blood   chemical messengers

Hormones are .... produced by glands known as .... glands.

Hormones travel in the .... to target organs. .... is a disease caused by too little of the hormone insulin.

2 **Homeostasis is the mechanism by which the body maintains a constant internal environment. Describe three things the body keeps constant.** (3 marks)

....

....

....

3 **On the diagram which letter shows** (4 marks)

a) the renal artery
b) the ureter
c) where urine is made
d) where urine is stored

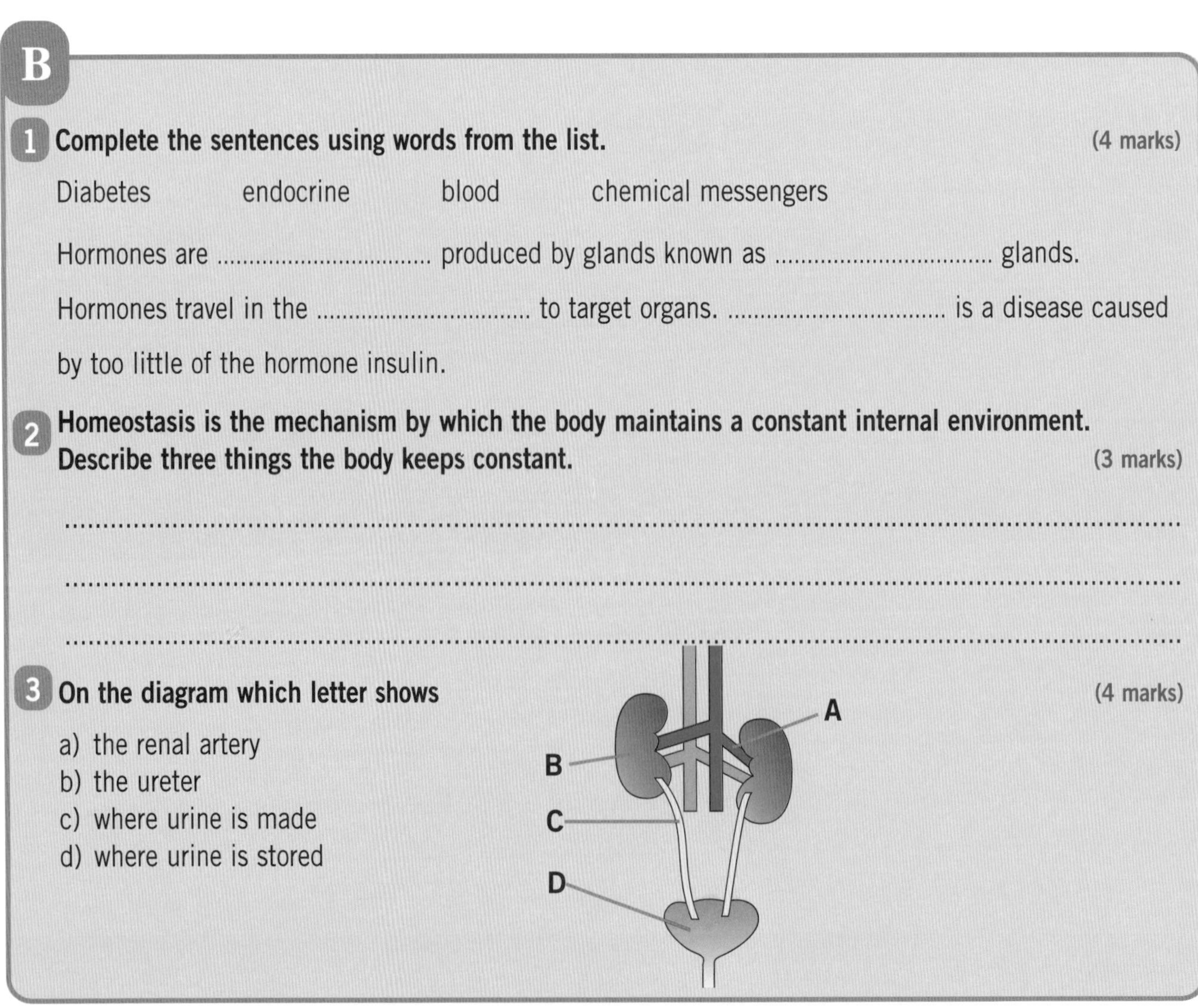

C

1 Complete the sentences using words from the list. (9 marks)

glucagon glucose glycogen high hormones insulin liver low normal

The pancreas is an organ involved in homeostasis; it maintains the level of .... (sugar) in the blood so that there is enough for respiration. The pancreas secretes two .... into the blood, insulin and glucagon. If blood sugar levels are too .... , which could be the case after a high carbohydrate meal, special cells in the pancreas detect these changes and release .... The .... responds to the amount of insulin in the blood and takes up glucose and stores it as .... Blood sugar levels return to ....
If blood sugar levels are too .... , which could be the case during exercise, the pancreas secretes .... This stimulates the conversion of stored glycogen in the liver back into glucose which is released into the blood. Blood sugar levels return to normal.

2 Three samples of liquid were taken, one from the blood entering the kidneys, one from the kidneys and one from the bladder. The samples were analysed to find the percentage of glucose, protein, urea and water present.

The results are shown in the table.

	Percentage of substance in		
Substance	**Blood**	**Filtrate in kidneys**	**Urine in bladder**
glucose	0.1	0.1	0.0
protein	9.0	0.0	0.0
urea	0.03	0.03	2.0
water	90.0	99.0	97.0

a) Which substance is present in the blood but not in the filtrate? (1 mark)

....

b) Which substance is more concentrated in the urine than the filtrate? (1 mark)

....

3 a) Complete the table to show characteristics of hormonal and nervous action. (3 marks)

Characteristic	Hormonal	Nervous
speed of action		
lasting effect		
where acts		

b) Which mechanism controls all homeostatic mechanisms? (1 mark)

....

How well did you do? 0-12 Try again 13-18 Getting there 19-24 Good work 25-31 Excellent!

The menstrual cycle

A

1 **Puberty is a time of** (1 mark)

a) change ☐
b) growth ☐
c) infancy ☐
d) middle age ☐

2 **The egg is released during which days in a typical menstrual cycle?** (1 mark)

a) 1–5 ☐
b) 5–14 ☐
c) 14–28 ☐
d) 28–5 ☐

3 **A typical menstrual cycle lasts how many days?** (1 mark)

a) 7 ☐
b) 14 ☐
c) 21 ☐
d) 28 ☐

4 **Name the hormone that maintains the uterus wall.** (1 mark)

a) insulin ☐
b) oestrogen ☐
c) progesterone ☐
d) testosterone ☐

5 **Which hormone can be used as an oral contraceptive?** (1 mark)

a) FSH ☐
b) oestrogen ☐
c) progesterone ☐
d) testosterone ☐

B

1 **Changes occur in the human body during puberty. Some occur in boys and girls, whilst others only occur in one of the sexes. Place a tick in the box to show which change happens to which sex.** (8 marks)

Change	Boys	Girls
breasts develop		
genitals develop		
hair grows under the arms		
hair grows on the face and body		
menstruation begins		
pubic hair grows		
sperm production begins		
voice deepens		

2 **What are the two main jobs of the menstrual cycle?** (2 marks)

....

3 a) **Which glands secrete hormones which control the menstrual cycle?** (2 marks)

....

b) **Describe the functions of the hormones Follicle Stimulating Hormone and Luteinising Hormone.** (3 marks)

....

C

1 The diagram shows stages from a typical menstrual cycle.

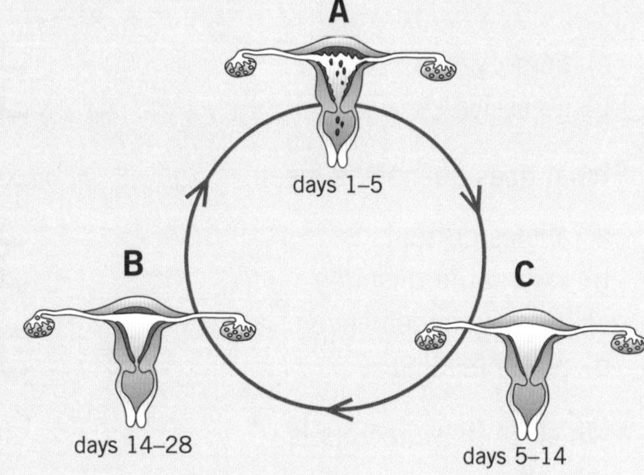

a) Which letter represents

i) ovulation ....

ii) uterus ready for implantation

....

iii) menstruation .... (3 marks)

b) Explain what happens during days 1–5 (2 marks)

....

....

....

....

c) The ovaries release oestrogen. What does it do? (3 marks)

....

....

....

....

2 a) FSH is called a 'fertility drug' Explain why. (2 marks)

....

....

....

b) What is a disadvantage of giving a woman FSH? (1 mark)

....

....

....

3 Progesterone is also produced during the menstrual cycle. What does it do and what happens when production stops? (2 marks)

....

....

....

....

4 IVF stands for in vitro fertilisation. What does it involve? (3 marks)

....

....

....

....

....

....

How well did you do? ✗ 0-12 Try again 13-19 Getting there 20-25 Good work 26-32 Excellent! ✓

Genetics and variation

A

1 Which allele always shows itself in the phenotype? (1 mark)

a) dominant ☐
b) heterozygous ☐
c) homozygous ☐
d) recessive ☐

2 Which word means the two alleles are the different? (1 mark)

a) dominant ☐
b) heterozygous ☐
c) homozygous ☐
d) recessive ☐

3 Which allele only shows itself in the homozygous phenotype? (1 mark)

a) dominant ☐
b) heterozygous ☐
c) homozygous ☐
d) recessive ☐

4 What does phenotype mean? (1 mark)

a) alleles present ☐
b) external fertilisation ☐
c) outward appearance of a gene ☐
d) pure breeding ☐

5 Which of these factors is inherited? (1 mark)

a) finger length ☐
b) playing the piano ☐
c) scars ☐
d) speaking Welsh ☐

B

1 Identical twins were separated at birth and brought up in different environments.

a) Name two features that would be identical in the twins (2 marks)

....

b) Name two features that could be different in identical twins (2 marks)

....

2 True or false? (3 marks)

	true	false
a) Living things that belong to the same species are all slightly different.	☐	☐
b) Variation can be between species or within species.	☐	☐
c) Genetics or the environment determines how we look and behave.	☐	☐

3 Complete the table by writing two examples in each box. (6 marks)

Inherited characteristic	Characteristic caused by the environment	Characteristic caused by the environment and genes

C

1 A gardener wanted to grow more geraniums. He collected the seeds of his plants and grew them. He also cut off growing tips of healthy plants and placed them in compost and they grew.

a) Why did the plants that grew from seeds produce different colour flowers? (3 marks)

....

....

b) Describe and explain the flower colour of the plants grown from cuttings. (2 marks)

....

....

c) What name is given to the plants grown from cuttings? (1 mark)

....

....

2 Mendel carried out some of the first breeding experiments using pea plants.

He grew tall and dwarf plants.

He cross pollinated a heterozygous tall plant with a homozygous dwarf plant.

He collected the seeds, germinated them and grew them into pea plants.

Use T for a tall allele and t for a dwarf allele

a) What is an allele? (1 mark)

....

b) What is the genotype of the heterozygous tall plant? (1 mark)

....

c) Draw a genetic diagram for this cross. (3 marks)

d) Tall is the dominant characteristic. Explain why. (1 mark)

....

....

3 We all look different because of the way our genes are inherited and the environment.

Name four features that are due entirely to our genetics. (4 marks)

....

....

....

....

4 Plants are affected by environmental factors. Name four environmental factors that could affect plants. (4 marks)

....

....

....

....

....

....

How well did you do? ✗ 0-15 Try again 16-22 Getting there 23-30 Good work 31-38 Excellent! ✓

Genetics

A

1 **Which monk discovered the principles behind genetics?** (1 mark)

a) Jenner ❑
b) Mendel ❑
c) Newton ❑
d) Pasteur ❑

2 **Which disease can be inherited?** (1 mark)

a) chickenpox ❑
b) common cold ❑
c) cystic fibrosis ❑
d) german measles ❑

3 **What are genes made of?** (1 mark)

a) amino acids ❑
b) chromosomes ❑
c) DNA ❑
d) fats ❑

4 **Which human problem may be treated in the future using gene therapy?** (1 mark)

a) measles ❑
b) cystic fibrosis ❑
c) short sight ❑
d) deafness ❑

5 **Which organism is used to produce genetically modified human insulin?** (1 mark)

a) bacteria ❑
b) fungi ❑
c) insects ❑
d) viruses ❑

B

1 **The human genome project was completed in 2003.**

a) What was its aim? (1 mark)

....

b) The project could help the sufferers of some diseases. Name two of these diseases. (2 marks)

....

c) Describe the benefits to the sufferers of these diseases. (2 marks)

....

2 **Write about four benefits of genetic engineering.** (4 marks)

....

....

....

3 **A person's DNA fingerprint is unique.**

a) Which branch of science uses this technique? (1 mark)

....

b) How is DNA fingerprinting used by the police? (2 marks)

....

C

1 a) **Peas can be round or wrinkled. Complete the punnet square.** (4 marks)

R represents the dominant allele, round and r represents the recessive allele, wrinkled.

	r	r
R		
r		

b) **What type of pea would these genotypes code for?** (4 marks)

i) RR ....

ii) Rr ....

iii) rR ....

iv) rr ....

2 a) **A child who suffers from cystic fibrosis has a faulty gene. They could be helped by gene therapy. What is gene therapy?** (1 mark)

....

....

....

b) **Describe what the doctors would try to do.** (1 mark)

....

....

....

....

c) **What problems might they encounter?** (2 marks)

....

....

....

3 a) **What is a transgenic animal?** (1 mark)

....

....

....

....

....

b) **Give an example of a transgenic animal.** (2 marks)

....

....

....

....

....

c) **It is possible to create a baby with specific features.**

What is the called and how is it done (2 marks)

....

....

....

....

....

....

....

How well did you do? ✗ 0-13 Try again 14-20 Getting there 21-27 Good work 28-34 Excellent! ✓

Inherited diseases

A

1 Uncontrolled jerky movements are a symptom of which disease? (1 mark)

a) chickenpox ☐
b) cystic fibrosis ☐
c) Huntington's disease ☐
d) german measles ☐

2 Which disease affects the brain? (1 mark)

a) measles ☐
b) Huntington's disease ☐
c) leukaemia ☐
d) sickle cell anaemia ☐

3 Name the cell that has not yet specialised. (1 mark)

a) blood ☐
b) nerve ☐
c) stem ☐
d) sperm ☐

4 Which of these diseases is an hereditary disease? (1 mark)

a) bronchitis ☐
b) cancer ☐
c) haemophilia ☐
d) obesity ☐

5 What is an inherited disease? (1 mark)

a) disease caused by microbes ☐
b) disease passed from person to person ☐
c) disease passed on from parent to child genetically ☐
d) self-inflicted disease ☐

B

1 Huntington's disease affects one in 20 000 people, so is a rare disease. 1 in 20 people are carriers of this disease.

Huntington's disease is caused by a dominant allele (C).

The diagram shows a family tree.

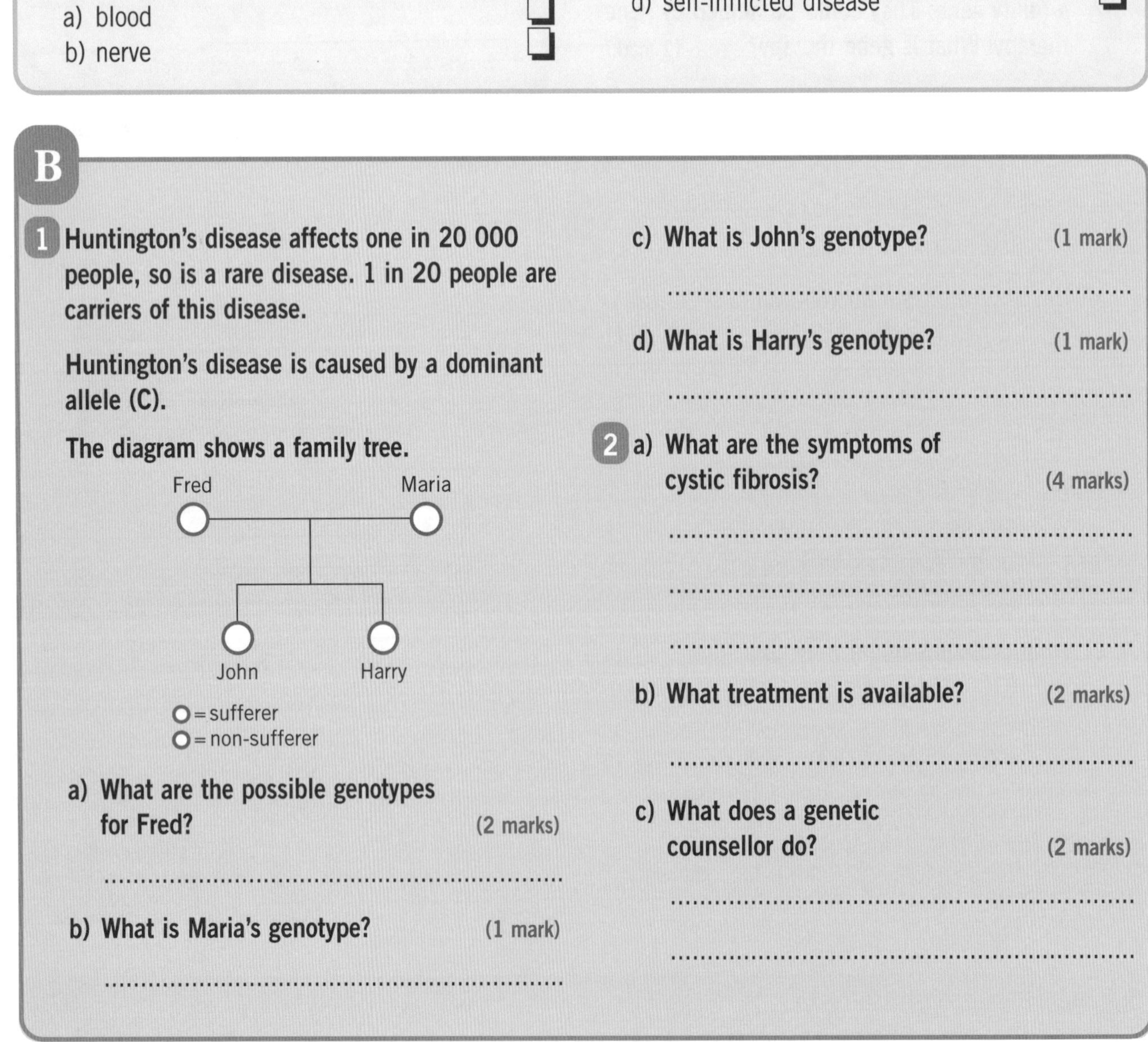

a) What are the possible genotypes for Fred? (2 marks)

....

b) What is Maria's genotype? (1 mark)

....

c) What is John's genotype? (1 mark)

....

d) What is Harry's genotype? (1 mark)

....

2 a) What are the symptoms of cystic fibrosis? (4 marks)

....

....

....

b) What treatment is available? (2 marks)

....

c) What does a genetic counsellor do? (2 marks)

....

....

C

1 a) Cystic fibrosis is caused by a recessive allele, carried by about one person in 20.

The genotype of a sufferer is cc.

i What are the possible genotypes of a non-sufferer? (2 marks)

....

ii What is the genotype of a carrier? (1 mark)

....

iii What is a carrier? (3 marks)

....

....

....

....

iv What is the probability of two carriers having a child that suffers? (1 mark)

....

v What is the probability of two carriers having a child that is a carrier? (1 mark)

....

2 Why do sufferers of Huntington's disease pass the disease on without knowing they have it? (2 marks)

....

....

....

....

3 a) What is genetic screening? (1 mark)

....

....

b) What are the benefits of genetic screening (2 marks)

....

....

....

....

4 a) What potential do stem cells have in treating inherited disease? (2 marks)

....

....

b) Stem cell research is in its infancy. What is needed to expand the research programme? (3 marks)

....

....

....

c) Why is stem cell research controversial? (1 mark)

....

d) Name two specific ways in which stem cell therapy can help humans. (2 marks)

....

....

How well did you do? 0-15 Try again 16-23 Getting there 24-31 Good work 32-39 Excellent!

Selective breeding

A

1 Which problem did scientists encounter when cloning Dolly, the sheep? (1 mark)

a) disease ☐
b) lack of eggs ☐
c) long life ☐
d) tissue rejection ☐

2 Scientists take a few cells from a plant and grow them into a new plant. What is this called? (1 mark)

a) cloning ☐
b) cuttings ☐
c) tissue culture ☐
d) variation ☐

3 What is a clone? (1 mark)

a) animals that live together ☐
b) genetically identical organisms ☐
c) organisms that are similar ☐
d) plants with no flowers ☐

4 What is artificial selection? (1 mark)

a) breeding for specific characteristics ☐
b) mapping the human genome ☐
c) producing artificial chemicals ☐
d) taking cuttings ☐

5 Selective breeding is another name for (1 mark)

a) artificial selection ☐
b) evolution ☐
c) natural selection ☐
d) variation ☐

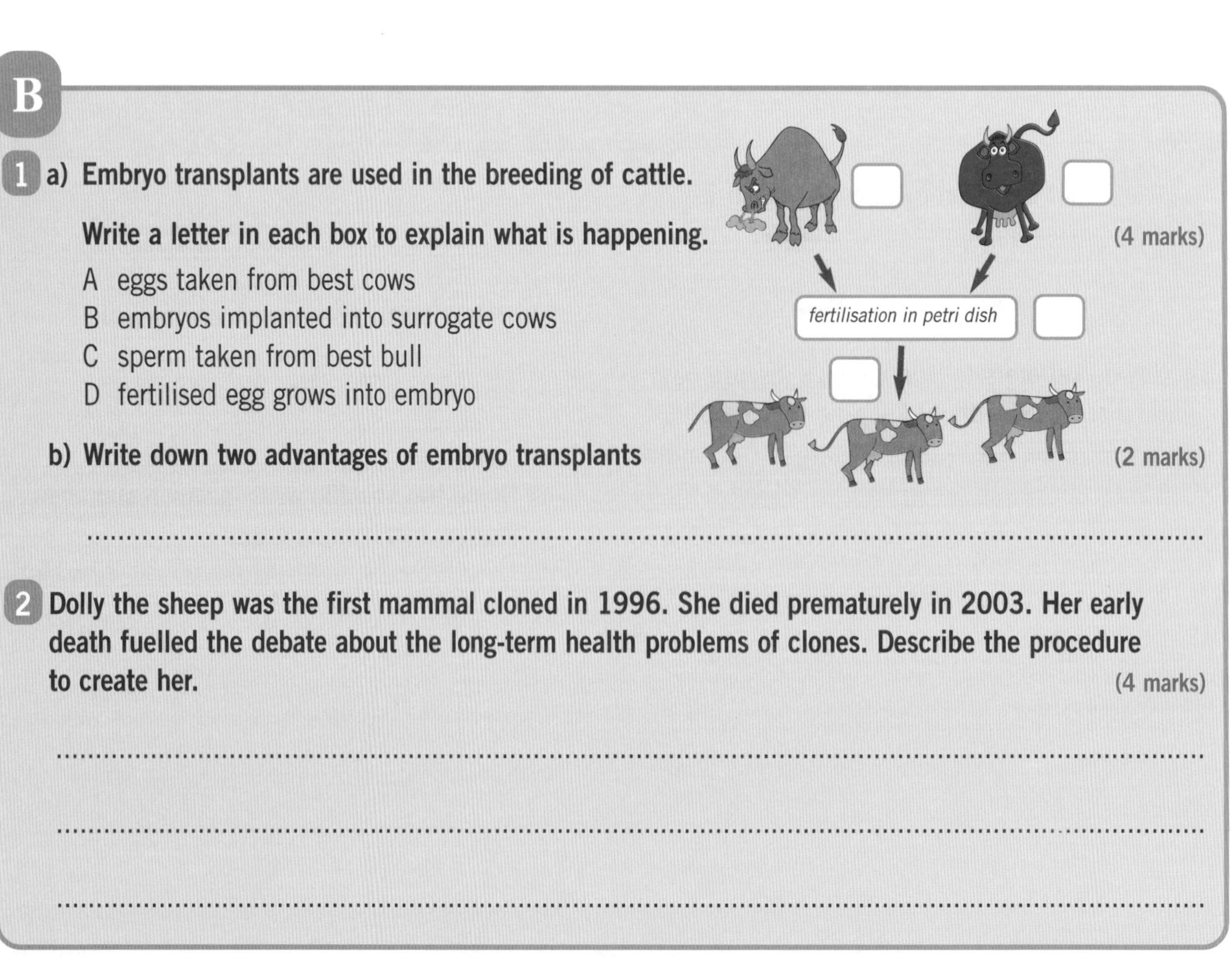

B

1 a) Embryo transplants are used in the breeding of cattle.

Write a letter in each box to explain what is happening. (4 marks)

A eggs taken from best cows
B embryos implanted into surrogate cows
C sperm taken from best bull
D fertilised egg grows into embryo

b) Write down two advantages of embryo transplants (2 marks)

....

2 Dolly the sheep was the first mammal cloned in 1996. She died prematurely in 2003. Her early death fuelled the debate about the long-term health problems of clones. Describe the procedure to create her. (4 marks)

....

....

....

C

1 The sentences describe the stages involved in artificial selection.

They are in the wrong order.

Using the letters, write the correct order in the boxes. (5 marks)

P Breed them together using sexual reproduction.
Q Repeated over generations
R All offspring have the desired characteristics.
S Select the individuals with the best characteristics.
T The best offspring are selected and are bred together.

2 A grower had some scented roses.

He took some cuttings to produce more scented roses.

a) What type of reproduction is this? (1 mark)

....

b) Why did he use this type of reproduction? (1 mark)

....

3 a) If animals or plants are continually bred from the same best animals or plants, the animals and plants will all be very similar. What are the disadvantages of this? (3 marks)

....

....

....

....

b) Why is important to keep wild varieties/rare breeds alive? (1 mark)

....

4 a) Strawberries are bred for large tasty berries. Suggest why. (1 mark)

....

....

....

b) Once a large red strawberry has been grown, the plants can be grown by tissue culture.

The diagrams show some of the stages in the process.

Explain what is happening at each stage. (3 marks)

....

....

....

c) What are the advantages of growing plants by tissue culture (3 marks)

....

....

....

How well did you do? 0-13 Try again 14-19 Getting there 20-26 Good work 27-33 Excellent!

Pyramids

A

1 What does a pyramid of numbers tell us? (1 mark)

a) animals that live together ☐
b) number of organisms in a food chain ☐
c) organisms that are similar ☐
d) who eats who ☐

2 Why do food chains rarely have more than four or five links in them? (1 mark)

a) animals at the beginning are too big ☐
b) energy is lost ☐
c) producers cannot make enough food ☐
d) too many plants die ☐

3 What is the name for a level in a food chain? (1 mark)

a) first level ☐
b) floor level ☐
c) plant level ☐
d) trophic level ☐

4 What does a pyramid of biomass tell us? (1 mark)

a) animals that live together ☐
b) mass of organisms in a food chain ☐
c) organisms that are different ☐
d) who eats who ☐

5 How can we improve the efficiency of food production? (1 mark)

a) grow less food ☐
b) increase the number of links in a food chain ☐
c) grow more food ☐
d) reduce number of links in food chain ☐

B

1 a) Here is a food chain.

grass → rabbit → fox

In this chain there were 1000 grass plants, 10 rabbits and 1 fox.

Draw a pyramid of numbers for this food chain. (3 marks)

b) Another chain had 1 rose bush, 1000 greenfly and 10 ladybirds.

Draw a pyramid of numbers for this food chain. (3 marks)

c) Why is a pyramid of numbers misleading? (1 mark)

....

2 a) Growing a field of wheat is cheaper than rearing a field of cattle. Explain why. (1 mark)

....

b) How can the farmer improve the efficiency of his production? (2 marks)

....

....

C

1 a) Here is a pyramid of numbers.

Draw a pyramid of biomass for this food chain. (4 marks)

b) Biomass is calculated by multiplying the number of organisms by the mass of one organism. If there are 2000 caterpillars each having a mass of 2 grams. Calculate the biomass of caterpillars. (2 marks)

....

....

....

....

c) If the biomass of caterpillars is 4000 grams, what would you expect the biomass of hawks to be?

Circle your answer

greater lower same (1 mark)

2 The diagram shows a sheep and its energy gains and losses.

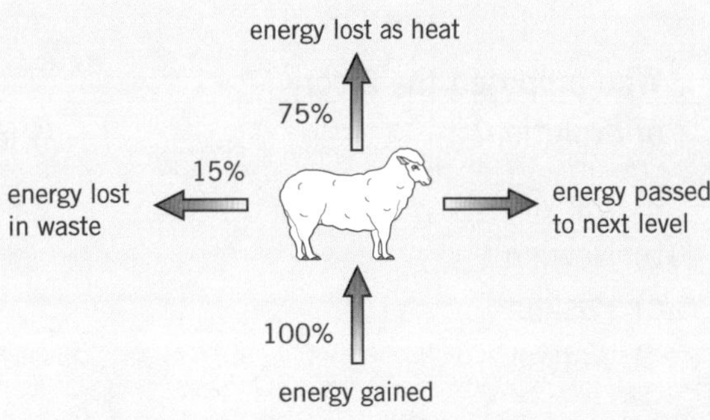

a) Calculate how much energy is passed on to the next level. (2 marks)

....

....

....

b) How is most energy lost from this sheep? (1 mark)

....

....

....

c) Suggest what form the waste might take (2 marks)

....

....

....

d) How is energy gained? (1 mark)

....

....

....

How well did you do? 0-11 Try again 12-16 Getting there 17-22 Good work 23-28 Excellent!

Evolution

EVOLUTION

Biology

A

1 **Who proposed the theory of evolution?** (1 mark)

a) Darwin ☐
b) Newton ☐
c) Pasteur ☐
d) Watson ☐

2 **What provides evidence for evolution?** (1 mark)

a) animals ☐
b) fossils ☐
c) plants ☐
d) viruses ☐

3 **What is another name for survival of the fittest?** (1 mark)

a) artificial selection ☐
b) natural selection ☐
c) sexual reproduction ☐
d) variation ☐

4 **What is extinction?** (1 mark)

a) new species being found ☐
b) no animals ☐
c) species dying out ☐
d) species hiding ☐

5 **What is a fossil?** (1 mark)

a) bones ☐
b) insects ☐
c) minerals ☐
d) remains of dead organisms ☐

B

1 **a) Name three factors that might prevent offspring surviving** (3 marks)

....

....

2 **a) Darwin visited the Galapagos Islands.**
Write down the four observations that he made which formed the basis of the theory of evolution. (4 marks)

....

....

....

b) What did Darwin conclude from these observations? (3 marks)

....

....

3 **What is a species?** (2 marks)

....

C

1 The peppered moth is an example of evolution.

There are two forms, one is dark in colour, the other is light-coloured.

They live in woodlands on lichen covered trees.

The light coloured moth was common before the industrial revolution.

a) Suggest how the dark coloured moth originated. (1 mark)

....

....

....

....

....

....

b) Why did the light coloured moth decline during the industrial revolution? (2 marks)

....

....

....

....

....

....

....

....

c) Why did the darker moth survive during the industrial revolution? (1 mark)

....

....

....

....

....

d) Now we have smoke free areas, what is happening to the numbers of dark and light coloured moths? (2 marks)

....

....

....

....

....

2 Explain how fossils are formed (4 marks)

....

....

....

....

....

....

....

....

....

....

....

How well did you do? ✗ 0-8 Try again 9-14 Getting there 15-21 Good work 22-27 Excellent! ✓

Adaptation and competition

A

1 What is a limiting factor? (1 mark)

a) something that increases the size of a population ☐
b) something that changes the gene pool ☐
c) something that stops a population becoming too large ☐
d) something that increases oxygen ☐

2 What does a camel store in its hump? (1 mark)

a) fat ☐
b) glucose ☐
c) protein ☐
d) water ☐

3 What are animals preparing for when they grow thick coats or store food? (1 mark)

a) death ☐
b) winter survival ☐
c) reproduction ☐
d) summer ☐

4 What do plants compete for that animals do not? (1 mark)

a) light ☐
b) nutrients ☐
c) space ☐
d) water ☐

5 Which feature would you find in a predator? (1 mark)

a) all round vision ☐
b) brightly coloured ☐
c) poor hearing ☐
d) sharp claws ☐

B

1 Match these words to their definitions.
Write your answers in the boxes. (4 marks)

community ecosystem habitat population

Definition	Word
where organism lives	
all one type of animal or plant	
living things in the habitat.	
all the living things and their physical environment.	

2 Name four factors that limit a population. (4 marks)

....

....

....

3 a) What is a predator?.. (1 mark)

b) What is prey? .... (1 mark)

C

1 a) Look at the picture of a polar bear.

Polar bears live in the arctic where it is very cold. They swim in freezing water.

Explain what features they have which adapt them to this environment. (5 marks)

....

....

....

....

....

....

....

....

....

....

....

....

....

....

2 The diagram shows the relationship between predator and prey.

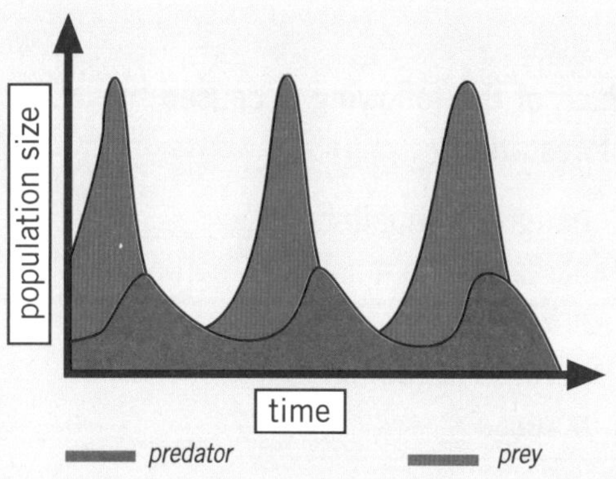

a) Describe the changes in prey population. (1 mark)

....

....

b) Describe the changes in predator population. (1 mark)

....

....

c) i) When does prey population decrease? (1 mark)

....

ii) Explain why. (1 mark)

....

d) i) What causes the prey population to increase? (1 mark)

....

ii) Explain why. (1 mark)

....

How well did you do? ✗ 0-10 Try again 11-15 Getting there 16-20 Good work 21-26 Excellent! ✓

Environmental damage 1

A

1 **Which of the following is caused by deforestation?** (1 mark)

a) increase in habitats ❑
b) increases the amount of carbon dioxide in the air ❑
c) increase in rainfall ❑
d) increase in soil erosion ❑

2 **Burning fossil fuel can lead to an increase in what?** (1 mark)

a) deforestation ❑
b) eutrophication ❑
c) greenhouse effect ❑
d) organic farming ❑

3 **What is used to help plants grow in organic farming?** (1 mark)

a) minerals ❑
b) manure ❑
c) NPK fertiliser ❑
d) pesticides ❑

4 **The amount of food produced is called** (1 mark)

a) conservation ❑
b) eutrophication ❑
c) productivity ❑
d) recycling ❑

5 **Which is not an alternative energy source?** (1 mark)

a) wave power ❑
b) fossil fuel ❑
c) solar power ❑
d) wind energy ❑

B

1 **Complete the sentences. Use words from the list.** (7 marks)

fertilisers food intensive minerals pesticides

Farming has had to become more .... to try and provide more .... from a given area of land. Many people regard this type of farming of animals as cruel. In order to produce more food from the land, ... and .... are needed. Chemicals called .... are used to kill pests. Farmers use .... to replace lost .... in the soil.

2 **Describe what happens when fertilisers are washed into rivers.** (5 marks)

....

....

....

C

1 Look at the diagram.

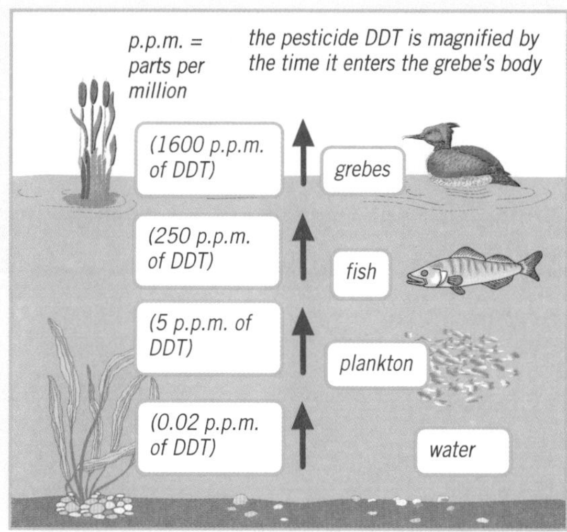

a) Explain how the pesticide gets into the food chain. (3 marks)

....

....

....

b) How much DDT is in the plankton? (1 mark)

....

2 A tomato grower wanted to kill the red spider mites which were eating his tomato plants.

He introduced another predatory mite into his greenhouses.

a) How would this help the grower to get rid of the red spider mites? (1 mark)

....

b) What is this type of control called? (1 mark)

....

c) What are the advantages of this sort of control? (2 marks)

....

....

....

d) What are the disadvantages of this sort of control? (1 mark)

....

....

....

3 a) Name three ways in which pollutants can spread. (3 marks)

....

....

....

b) What name is given to animals and plants that show pollution (1 mark)

....

c) Which two animals show polluted water (2 marks)

....

....

d) Which types of organisms show air pollution? (2 marks)

....

....

How well did you do? ✗ 0-10 Try again 11-15 Getting there 16-20 Good work 21-26 Excellent! ✓

Environmental damage 2

A

1 Which gas contributes to the greenhouse effect? (1 mark)

a) chlorine ❑
b) methane ❑
c) nitrogen ❑
d) oxygen ❑

2 What is a pollutant? (1 mark)

a) substance that is useful to living things ❑
b) substance that comes from the earth ❑
c) substance that is harmful to living things ❑
d) substance that is made by animals ❑

3 What is sustainable development? (1 mark)

a) keeping things the same ❑
b) looking after the earth for the future ❑
c) monitoring resources ❑
d) planting more trees ❑

4 Which element comes from car exhausts and can damage the nervous system? (1 mark)

a) chlorine ❑
b) lead ❑
c) nitrogen ❑
d) oxygen ❑

5 Soot comes from burning fossil fuels. It is deposited on the leaves of plants. What does it stop them from doing? (1 mark)

a) breathing ❑
b) excreting ❑
c) photosynthesising ❑
d) reproducing ❑

B

1 True or false? (5 marks)

	true	false
a) Burning fossil fuels is a cause of acid rain	❑	❑
b) Catalytic converters in cars increase emissions of harmful gases	❑	❑
c) Using unleaded petrol reduces lead compounds in the atmosphere	❑	❑
d) Carbon dioxide is a greenhouse gas	❑	❑
e) Water is chlorinated to remove viruses	❑	❑

2 Evidence is being collected that shows that the world is warming up.

a) What causes this? (1 mark)

....

b) What is this warming up called? (1 mark)

....

c) Look at the diagram.

Explain this warming up by using these words to fill in the spaces in the diagram (6 marks)

smaller more most less UV

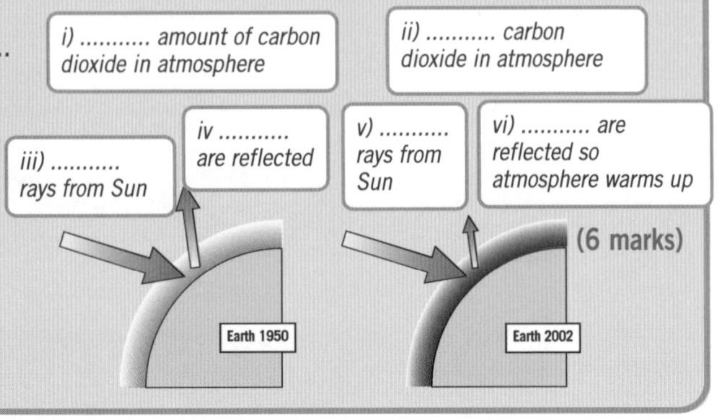

C

1 Look at the diagram. It shows some sources of pollutants of the air.

a) List three gases which pollute the air. (3 marks)

....

....

....

b) How do these gases contribute to acid rain? (3 marks)

....

....

....

c) What effect does acid rain have

i) on buildings (1 mark)

....

ii) on lakes (2 marks)

....

iii) on trees (1 mark)

....

2 a) What does CFC stand for? (1 mark)

....

b) Where do they come from? (1 mark)

....

c) What effect do they have in the atmosphere (2 marks)

....

....

d) What consequence can this have for humans? (1 mark)

....

3 As a result of the greenhouse effect, the world temperature is slowly rising.

This could cause the polar ice caps to melt, and sea levels could rise.

Suggest four ways in which you as an individual can help to slow down global warming. (4 marks)

....

....

....

....

....

....

....

....

How well did you do? 0-14 Try again 15-22 Getting there 23-29 Good work 30-37 Excellent!

Ecology and classification

A

1 What does an ecologist study? (1 mark)

a) effect of the sun ☐
b) living things in their habitat ☐
c) resources needed by humans ☐
d) results of planting more trees ☐

2 Who devised a system of classification? (1 mark)

a) Banting ☐
b) Best ☐
c) Linnaeus ☐
d) Darwin ☐

3 How many kingdoms are there now? (1 mark)

a) 2 ☐
b) 3 ☐
c) 4 ☐
d) 5 ☐

4 Which is an abiotic factor? (1 mark)

a) colour ☐
b) length of beak ☐
c) light intensity ☐
d) number of legs ☐

5 What bird did Darwin study on the Galapagos Islands? (1 mark)

a) blackbirds ☐
b) finches ☐
c) owls ☐
d) eagles ☐

B

1 a) When organisms are put into groups, they is an order of classification.
Here are the group names but in the wrong order.
Rewrite them in the correct order. (1 mark)

class family genus kingdom order phylum species

....

b) What is a species? (2 marks)

....

c) In the scientific world, each type of organism is given a name made of two parts.

What system of naming is this? .... (1 mark)

d) Why is a scientific name used? .... (2 marks)

e) What is the scientific name for humans? .... (2 marks)

2 Name the five groups of vertebrates. (5 marks)

....

....

C

1 Use this key to identify these four organisms. (4 marks)

P Q R S

START HERE

Does it have legs?
Yes → Does it have 6 legs? Yes → Beetle; No → Spider
No → Does it have a shell? Yes → Snail; No → Slug

P is ....

Q is ....

R is ....

S is ....

2 a) What is an ecosystem? (4 marks)

....

....

....

....

....

b) Name two natural ecosystems? (2 marks)

....

....

3 Here are diagrams of various apparatus to sample living organisms.

A B C

a) Name the pieces of apparatus. (3 marks)

A – ....

B – ....

C – ....

b) The field is 100 m long and 100m wide. Apparatus A was thrown randomly 10 times and each time the number of daisies inside was counted. The size of A was 1 m by 1 m. The results were 4, 5, 2, 8, 11, 9, 3, 5, 10, 3.

Calculate the estimated number of daisies in the field. (6 marks)

....

....

....

....

....

....

....

How well did you do? ✗ 0-14 Try again 15-22 Getting there 23-29 Good work 30-37 Excellent! ✓

Limestone

A

1 **What type of rock is limestone?** (1 mark)

a) sedimentary ❑
b) metamorphic ❑
c) igneous ❑
d) mineral ❑

2 **What type of reaction occurs when limestone is heated?** (1 mark)

a) exothermic ❑
b) neutralisation ❑
c) thermal decomposition ❑
d) displacement ❑

3 **What gas is given off when calcium carbonate is heated?** (1 mark)

a) carbon monoxide ❑
b) oxygen ❑
c) nitrogen ❑
d) carbon dioxide ❑

4 **Heating a mixture of limestone, sand and soda produces a useful new substance. What is this substance called?** (1 mark)

a) concrete ❑
b) cement ❑
c) glass ❑
d) quicklime ❑

5 **What is a solution of slaked lime called?** (1 mark)

a) limewater ❑
b) quicklime ❑
c) limestone ❑
d) calcium oxide ❑

B

1 **Complete the table below to show how each substance is made. The first one is done for you.** (5 marks)

Substance	How it is made
concrete	by mixing cement, sand, rock chippings and water.
a)	by heating limestone.
b)	by roasting powdered clay and powdered limestone.
c)	by mixing cement, sand and water.
d)	by adding water to quicklime.
e)	by heating limestone, sand and soda.

2 **True or false?** (5 marks)

	true	false
a) Powdered limestone can be used to neutralise the acidity in lakes caused by acid rain.	❑	❑
b) The main chemical compound in limestone is calcium oxide.	❑	❑
c) Concrete is strong but very expensive.	❑	❑
d) Slaked lime will neutralise the acidity in lakes faster than powdered limestone.	❑	❑
e) When calcium oxide is reacted with water, the product is calcium carbonate.	❑	❑

C

1 When sodium hydrogen carbonate is heated, it reacts to form sodium carbonate, carbon dioxide and water.

a) Balance this symbol equation to represent the reaction. (1 mark)

.... $NaHCO_3 \rightarrow Na_2CO_3 + CO_2 + H_2O$

b) Which everyday substance, usually found in the kitchen, contains sodium hydrogen carbonate? (1 mark)

....

....

....

2 When calcium carbonate is heated, it reacts to form calcium oxide and carbon dioxide.

a) Complete the symbol equation to represent this reaction. (2 marks)

$CaCO_3 \rightarrow$ .... + ...

b) Explain why this reaction could be described as an example of thermal decomposition. (2 marks)

....

....

....

....

....

3 Limestone can be made into slaked lime. The diagram below shows the steps involved in making slaked lime.

limestone → Step 1 → quicklime CaO → Step 2 → slaked lime $Ca(OH)_2$

a) What is the formula of calcium carbonate? (1 mark)

....

....

b) In step 1 the calcium carbonate is heated to produce quicklime. Name the other product of this reaction. (1 mark)

....

....

c) What is the chemical name of quicklime? (1 mark)

....

....

d) In step 2 which substance is added to quicklime to produce slaked lime? (1 mark)

....

e) What is the chemical name of slaked lime? (1 mark)

....

....

How well did you do? ✗ 0-10 Try again 11-15 Getting there 16-20 Good work 21-26 Excellent! ✓

Fuels

A

1 Which of these substances could be classified as fossil fuels? (1 mark)

a) coal and uranium ❑
b) solar and wind ❑
c) wave and coal ❑
d) coal and oil ❑

2 What is crude oil a mixture of? (1 mark)

a) plastics ❑
b) elements ❑
c) hydrocarbons ❑
d) solids ❑

3 Which of these options best describes a short chain hydrocarbon? (1 mark)

a) runny, hard to ignite and has a high boiling point ❑
b) viscous, hard to ignite and has a high boiling point ❑
c) viscous, easy to ignite and has a low boiling point ❑
d) runny, easy to ignite and has a low boiling point ❑

4 What are groups of hydrocarbon molecules with a similar number of carbon atoms called? (1 mark)

a) groups ❑
b) families ❑
c) sections ❑
d) fractions ❑

5 What is formed by the cracking of hydrocarbon molecules? (1 mark)

a) oxygen ❑
b) shorter hydrocarbon molecules ❑
c) longer hydrocarbon molecules ❑
d) pure carbon ❑

B

1 True or false? (5 marks)

	true	false
a) Crude oil is a mixture of hydrocarbons.	❑	❑
b) Hydrocarbons contain atoms of hydrogen, carbon and oxygen only.	❑	❑
c) A hydrocarbon molecule with 15 carbon atoms is found in the petrol fraction.	❑	❑
d) Fractional distillation can be used to separate a mixture of hydrocarbons.	❑	❑
e) Long chain hydrocarbon molecules make useful fuels.	❑	❑

2 Cross out the incorrect word/phrase in the following sentences. (5 marks)

a) Crude oil can be separated by filtering/fractional distillation.
b) It is hotter at the top/bottom of a fractionating column.
c) Long/short hydrocarbon molecules reach the top of the fractionating column before they condense.
d) Long hydrocarbon molecules are useful/not useful as fuels.
e) Long hydrocarbon molecules can be broken down into smaller hydrocarbon molecules by cracking/distilling.

C

1 Crude oil is extracted from the Earth's crust. It is a mixture of many substances; the most important ones are hydrocarbons. Propane is obtained from crude oil. It can be used as a fuel. This diagram represents one molecule of propane.

```
  H H H
  | | |
H-C-C-C-H
  | | |
  H H H
```

a) Give the molecular formula of propane. (1 mark)

....

....

....

b) Is propane a hydrocarbon? Explain your answer. (1 mark)

....

....

....

....

....

....

c) Crude oil can be separated using fractional distillation. The large hydrocarbon molecules separated during fractional distillation are not very useful. These large hydrocarbon molecules can be broken down into smaller, more useful hydrocarbons by cracking. Cracking is an example of a thermal decomposition reaction. Explain why this reaction can be described as an example of thermal decomposition. (1 mark)

....

....

....

....

....

....

d) A decane, ($C_{10}H_{22}$) molecule can be split into two smaller molecules by cracking.

i) Complete the equation to show this reaction.

$C_{10}H_{22} \rightarrow$ .... + C_2H_4 (1 mark)

ii) Name the product of the cracking of decane which has the formula C_2H_4 (1 mark)

....

iii) What is C_2H_4 used to make? (1 mark)

....

....

....

How well did you do? ✗ 0-8 Try again 9-12 Getting there 13-16 Good work 17-21 Excellent! ✓

Organic families

A

1 **How many bonds do carbon atoms have the ability to form?** (1 mark)

a) 1 ☐
b) 2 ☐
c) 3 ☐
d) 4 ☐

2 **What is the name given to saturated hydrocarbons?** (1 mark)

a) alkenes ☐
b) alkanes ☐
c) alcohols ☐
d) esters ☐

3 **What is the test for an alkene?** (1 mark)

a) it has carbon and hydrogen atoms only ☐
b) it can be burnt ☐
c) it decolourises bromine water ☐
d) it does not react with bromine water ☐

4 **Which of these molecules is an alkane?** (1 mark)

a) CH_4 ☐
b) C_2H_5OH ☐
c) C_2H_4 ☐
d) CH_3OH ☐

5 **Which of these molecules is an alkene?** (1 mark)

a) CH_4 ☐
b) C_2H_5OH ☐
c) C_2H_4 ☐
d) CH_3OH ☐

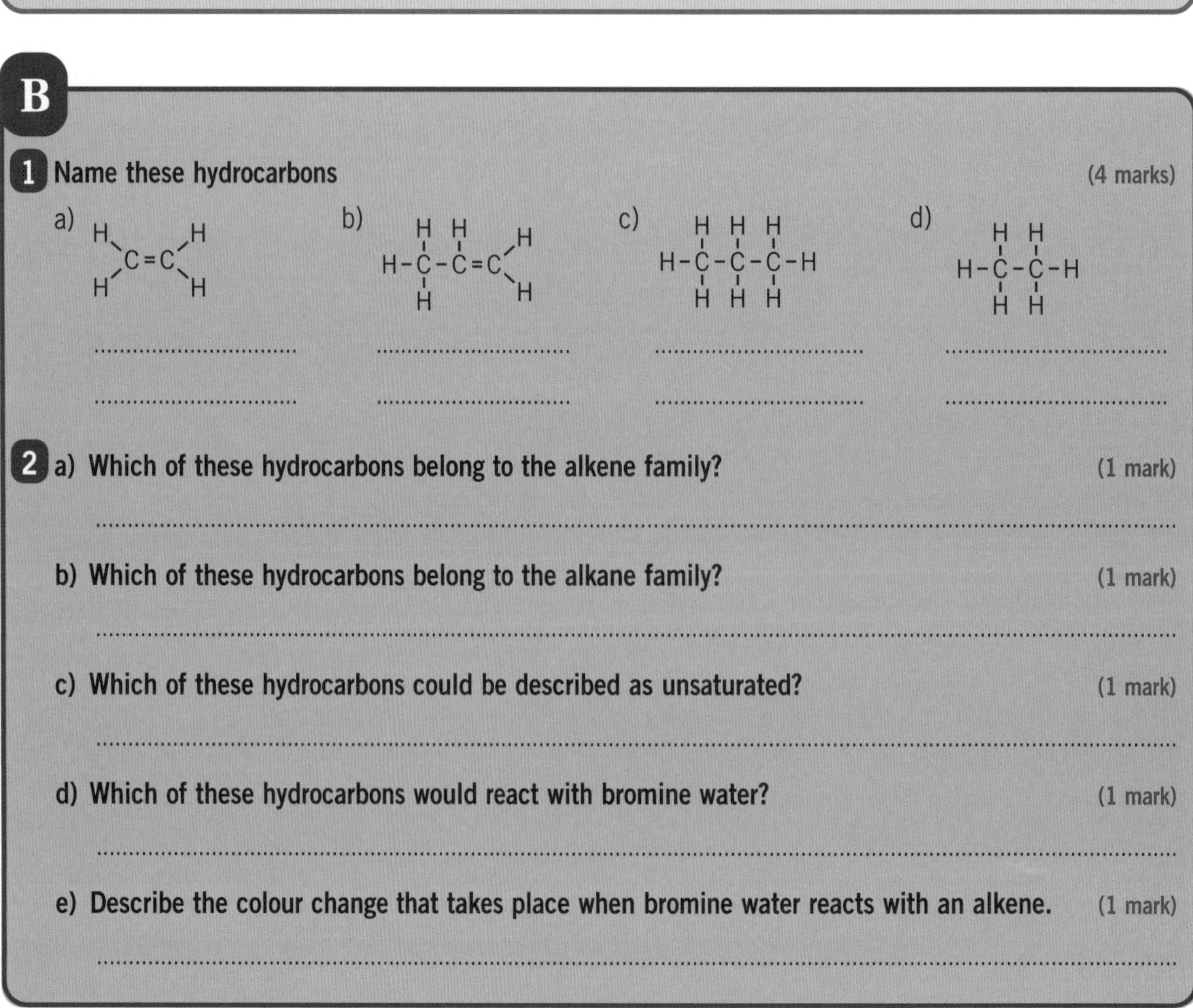

B

1 **Name these hydrocarbons** (4 marks)

```
a)  H     H        b)  H  H     H      c)   H  H  H        d)  H  H
     \   /             |  |    /            |  |  |            |  |
      C=C            H-C--C=C            H-C--C--C-H        H-C--C-H
     /   \             |       \            |  |  |            |  |
    H     H            H        H           H  H  H            H  H
```

a) ....
b) ....
c) ....
d) ....

2 **a) Which of these hydrocarbons belong to the alkene family?** (1 mark)

....

b) Which of these hydrocarbons belong to the alkane family? (1 mark)

....

c) Which of these hydrocarbons could be described as unsaturated? (1 mark)

....

d) Which of these hydrocarbons would react with bromine water? (1 mark)

....

e) Describe the colour change that takes place when bromine water reacts with an alkene. (1 mark)

....

C

1 **Carbon atoms form four bonds with other atoms.**

This means that carbon atoms can be made into an enormous range of compounds.

These three molecules all contain atoms of the element carbon.

molecule A

```
  H H
  | |
H-C-C-O-H
  | |
  H H
```

molecule B

```
  H H H
  | | |
H-C-C-C-H
  | | |
  H H H
```

molecule C

```
  H H H
  | | |
H-C-C=C-H
  |
  H
```

a) Is molecule A a hydrocarbon?
Explain your answer. (1 mark)

b) Is molecule B saturated?
Explain your answer. (1 mark)

c) State the name of molecule B. (1 mark)

d) Which family of organic compounds does molecule C belong to? (1 mark)

e) State the name of molecule C. (1 mark)

molecule D

```
  H H H H
  | | | |
H-C-C-C=C
  | |   |
  H H   H
```

f) Which family of organic compounds does molecule D belong to? (1 mark)

g) State the name of molecule D. (1 mark)

How well did you do? ✗ 0-8 Try again 9-12 Getting there 13-16 Good work 17-21 Excellent! ✓

Vegetable oils

A

1 Which vitamins can we get from plant oils? (1 mark)

a) C and A ❑
b) A and D ❑
c) C and B ❑
d) A and K ❑

2 Oils can be extracted from plants. Which of these parts of plants are least likely to yield oils? (1 mark)

a) fruits ❑
b) stalks ❑
c) seeds ❑
d) nuts ❑

3 Which of these ways of cooking potatoes would you expect to produce food which has the highest energy content? (1 mark)

a) baking ❑
b) boiling ❑
c) frying ❑
d) microwaving ❑

4 Which of these foods contains plant oil? (1 mark)

a) bacon ❑
b) olive oil ❑
c) cream ❑
d) butter ❑

5 What is the catalyst used in the hydrogenation of plant oils? (1 mark)

a) nickel ❑
b) platinum ❑
c) gold ❑
d) sodium ❑

B

1 True or false? (5 marks)

	true	false
a) Salad dressing is an example of an emulsion.	❑	❑
b) Salad dressing is a mixture of alcohol and water.	❑	❑
c) Hydrophobic means attracted to water	❑	❑
d) Hydrophilic means attracted to water	❑	❑
e) Emulsifiers are molecules that help to keep the oil and water in mayonnaise mixed together.	❑	❑

2 Complete the table to show the name of the type of chemical added to food. The first one is done for you. (4 marks)

Name of the chemical	Description of the chemical
colours	added to make the food look more attractive.
a)	added to decrease the amount of sugar used.
b)	added to enhance taste.
c)	added to help ingredients mix together.
d)	chemicals that are approved for use throughout the EU.

C

1 This label was taken from the side of a tub of low fat spread.

Ingredients:
Vegetable oils, hydrogenated vegetable oils, water, salt, emulsifier, preservative, colours, Vitamins A and D.

a) From which parts of a plant can vegetable oil be extracted? Tick two boxes. (2 marks)

- roots ☐
- seeds ☐
- leaves ☐
- nuts ☐
- flowers ☐

b) Why should people be careful about the amount of fat that they eat? (1 mark)

....

....

....

....

c) Animal fats are usually solid at room temperature. Vegetable fats are usually liquid at room temperature.

Vegetable oil is liquid

Butter is solid

i) What type of bond is present in vegetable fats that mean that they are liquid at room temperature? (1 mark)

....

....

....

....

ii) What would you add to test for the presence of this bond? (1 mark)

....

....

....

....

iii) What would you see? (1 mark)

....

....

....

....

d) Emulsifiers are molecules that help water and oil to mix. One end of an emulsifier molecule is attracted to oil. What is the other end of the molecule attracted to? (1 mark)

....

....

....

....

How well did you do? 0-8 Try again 9-12 Getting there 13-16 Good work 17-21 Excellent!

Plastics

A

1 **What is the monomer used to produce polythene?** (1 mark)

a) ethane ☐
b) ethene ☐
c) propene ☐
d) polymer ☐

2 **What is the monomer used to produce PVC?** (1 mark)

a) ethane ☐
b) chloroethene ☐
c) ethene ☐
d) tetrafluoroethene ☐

3 **What is the monomer used to produce Teflon?** (1 mark)

a) ethane ☐
b) chloroethene ☐
c) ethene ☐
d) tetrafluoroethene ☐

4 **What is the monomer used to produce polypropene?** (1 mark)

a) ethane ☐
b) ethene ☐
c) propene ☐
d) polymer ☐

5 **Which polymer is used to make crates?** (1 mark)

a) polypropene ☐
b) polystyrene ☐
c) PVC ☐
d) polythene ☐

B

1 **The diagrams on the right show three different hydrocarbons.**

molecule A	molecule B	molecule C
H–C–H with H above and H below (C bonded to four H)	$H_2C=CH_2$ (C=C, each C bonded to two H)	C=C with H and CH_3 above, H and H below

a) Which of these hydrocarbons represents a saturated hydrocarbon? .... (1 mark)

b) What is the name of molecule A? .... (1 mark)

c) Lots of molecules of 'molecule C' could be joined together to form a polymer. What is the name of this polymer? (1 mark)

....

2 **True or false?** (5 marks)

	true	false
a) Ethane is a monomer that can be made into polythene.	☐	☐
b) 'Poly' means three.	☐	☐
c) PVC is useful because it is flexible.	☐	☐
d) Ethene is made into polythene by heating many ethene molecules with a catalyst under high pressure.	☐	☐
e) The monomers used to make addition polymers have double bonds.	☐	☐

C

1 Polytetrafluoroethene, PTFE can be used to make non-stick saucepans.

PTFE is made by the polymerisation of tetrafluoroethene.

a) Is PTFE a hydrocarbon?
Explain your answer. (1 mark)

....

....

....

....

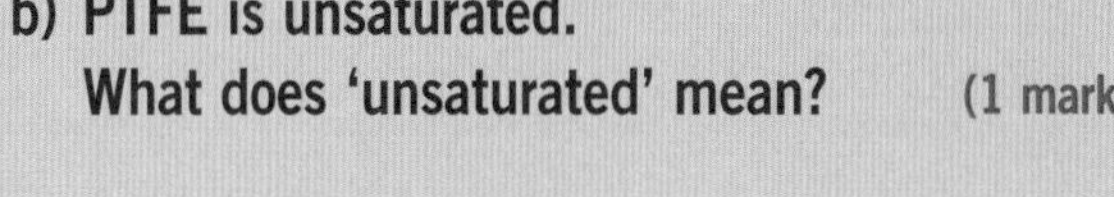

b) PTFE is unsaturated.
What does 'unsaturated' mean? (1 mark)

....

....

....

....

c) How could you prove that PTFE is unsaturated?

i) What would you do? (1 mark)

....

....

....

ii) What would you see? (1 mark)

....

....

....

d) Which of these equations shows the polymerisation of tetrafluoroethene? (1 mark)

i)
$$n\ \begin{matrix} F & & F \\ | & & | \\ C & = & C \\ | & & | \\ F & & F \end{matrix} \longrightarrow \left(\begin{matrix} & F & & F & \\ & | & & | & \\ - & C & = & C & - \\ & | & & | & \\ & F & & F & \end{matrix} \right)_n$$

ii)
$$n\ \begin{matrix} F & & F \\ | & & | \\ C & = & C \\ | & & | \\ F & & F \end{matrix} \longrightarrow \left(\begin{matrix} & F & & F & \\ & | & & | & \\ - & C & - & C & - \\ & | & & | & \\ & F & & F & \end{matrix} \right)_n$$

iii)
$$n\ \begin{matrix} F & & F \\ | & & | \\ C & - & C \\ | & & | \\ F & & F \end{matrix} \longrightarrow \left(\begin{matrix} & F & & F & \\ & | & & | & \\ - & C & - & C & - \\ & | & & | & \\ & F & & F & \end{matrix} \right)_n$$

iv)
$$n\ \begin{matrix} F & & F \\ | & & | \\ C & = & C \\ | & & | \\ F & & F \end{matrix} \longrightarrow \begin{matrix} F & & F \\ | & & | \\ C & = & C \\ | & & | \\ F & & F \end{matrix}\ n$$

....

....

e) When they are thrown away objects made from PTFE do not break down. Why don't they break down? (1 mark)

....

....

....

....

....

How well did you do? ✗ 0-7 Try again 8-11 Getting there 12-15 Good work 16-19 Excellent! ✓

Ethanol

A

1 What is the formula of ethanol? (1 mark)

a) CH_3OH ☐
b) C_2H_6 ☐
c) C_2H_4 ☐
d) C_2H_5OH ☐

2 Alcohol can be made from glucose what is the formula of glucose? (1 mark)

a) $C_6H_{12}O_6$ ☐
b) $C_6H_6O_{12}$ ☐
c) $C_{12}O_6H_6$ ☐
d) $C_6H_{12}O_{12}$ ☐

3 What is the name of the process in which glucose is converted to alcohol? (1 mark)

a) distillation ☐
b) filtration ☐
c) fermentation ☐
d) cracking ☐

4 What is the catalyst used when glucose is converted to ethanol? (1 mark)

a) sugar ☐
b) heat ☐
c) yeast ☐
d) bacteria ☐

5 What are the conditions used in to make industrial alcohol? (1 mark)

a) yeast and room temperature ☐
b) yeast and phosphoric acid ☐
c) yeast and a temperature of 300°C ☐
d) phosphoric acid and a temperature of 300°C ☐

B

1 Complete the following passages. (12 marks)

Ethanol is a member of the .... organic family. Ethanol has many useful .... Many perfumes contain ethanol. It is a good solvent so things .... well in ethanol. Ethanol has a .... boiling point so it quickly .... from the skin.

In some countries ethanol made from sugar beet or sugarcane is used as a .... The ethanol is a .... energy source. Unfortunately, burning alcohol releases .... energy than burning petrol.

Traditionally, alcohol has been produced by .... During fermentation glucose found in fruit, vegetables and .... is converted into alcohol and carbon .... The reaction is catalysed by ....

2 True or false? (5 marks)

	true	false
a) Methanol is toxic.	☐	☐
b) 'Meths' contains ethanol and methanol.	☐	☐
c) During fermentation, the higher the temperature the faster the rate at which ethanol is produced.	☐	☐
d) Yeast contains enzymes.	☐	☐
e) Ethane is used in the industrial production of ethanol.	☐	☐

C

1 A chemical reaction can convert glucose into two useful new substances.

$$C_6H_{12}O_6 \rightarrow 2C_2H_5OH + 2CO_2$$

a) Name the useful product with the formula C_2H_5OH (1 mark)

....

....

b) Name the useful product with the formula CO_2 (1 mark)

....

....

2 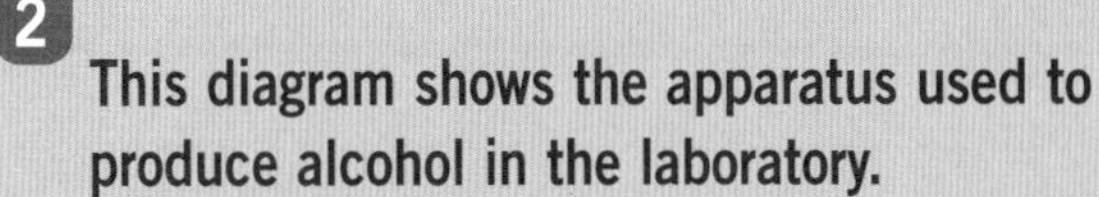

This diagram shows the apparatus used to produce alcohol in the laboratory.

a) What is this process called? (1 mark)

....

....

....

....

b) What is the name of the substance added to catalyse the reaction? (1 mark)

....

....

....

....

c) Why is an airlock used during this process? (1 mark)

....

....

....

....

d) Alcohol can also be produced industrially. Long chain hydrocarbons are not useful as fuels. The cracking of long hydrocarbons produces shorter hydrocarbons that are useful as fuels and ethene molecules. Ethene molecules can be reacted with another chemical to produce alcohol. Complete the equation by adding the formula of the other reactant in this reaction. (1 mark)

$$C_2H_4 + \text{...........} \rightarrow C_2H_5OH$$

Evolution of the atmosphere

A

1 Which gases comprised the Earth's early atmosphere? (1 mark)

a) carbon dioxide, steam, ammonia and methane ❑
b) oxygen, nitrogen and trace amounts of carbon dioxide, water vapour and noble gases ❑
c) carbon monoxide and water vapour ❑
d) oxygen, nitrogen and carbon monoxide ❑

2 For how long have the levels of carbon dioxide in the atmosphere been rising? (1 mark)

a) since the last general election ❑
b) the last two hundred years (since the industrial revolution) ❑
c) since the middle ages ❑
d) the last twenty years ❑

3 How is the extra carbon dioxide in the atmosphere produced? (1 mark)

a) when fossil fuels are formed ❑
b) when fossil fuels are burnt ❑
c) when fossil fuels are mined ❑
d) when fossil fuels are buried ❑

4 Which gases comprise the Earth's atmosphere today? (1 mark)

a) carbon dioxide, steam, ammonia and methane ❑
b) oxygen, nitrogen and trace amounts of carbon dioxide, water vapour and noble gases ❑
c) carbon monoxide and water vapour ❑
d) oxygen, nitrogen and carbon monoxide ❑

5 Why is the ozone layer useful to us? (1 mark)

a) it stops acid rain ❑
b) it prevents global warming ❑
c) it filters out harmful UV rays ❑
d) it helps to reduce car crime ❑

B

1 Place these events in order to show how the Earth's atmosphere has evolved. (5 marks)

a) Plants evolved and soon colonised most of the Earth. ❑
b) Carbon dioxide became locked up as carbonate minerals and in fossil fuels. ❑
c) Enormous volcanic activity produced carbon dioxide, steam, ammonia and methane. ❑
d) Plants removed carbon dioxide and produced oxygen. ❑
e) The water vapour (steam) condensed to form the early oceans. ❑

2 True or false? (5 marks)

	true	false
a) Nitrogen is produced by denitrifying bacteria.	❑	❑
b) Earth's early atmosphere was similar to the modern day atmosphere of Neptune and Pluto.	❑	❑
c) Ammonia has the formula CH_4.	❑	❑
d) The evolution of green plants lead to a decrease in the amount of oxygen and an increase in the amount of carbon dioxide in the atmosphere.	❑	❑
e) Carbon dioxide can be removed from the atmosphere by the reaction between carbon dioxide and seawater to produce insoluble carbonate salts and soluble calcium and magnesium hydrogen carbonate salts.	❑	❑

C

1 **This question is about how the amount of oxygen in the atmosphere has increased over time. Use the words and phrases in the box below to complete the sentences.** (4 marks)

carbon dioxide	ozone
harmful	plants

As a) .... evolved the amount of oxygen in the atmosphere increased. These plants grew well in the b) .... rich atmosphere. As the amount of oxygen increased an c) .... layer developed. This layer filtered out d) .... ultraviolet rays.

2 **Over time the composition of the Earth's atmosphere has changed. Scientists believe that the Earth is 4.5 billion years old. During the first billion years of the Earth's history there was enormous volcanic activity. These volcanoes released large amounts of gas which formed the Earth's early atmosphere.**

a) Which of these gases was NOT produced in large quantities by these volcanoes? Tick one box. (1 mark)

- methane ❑
- CFCs ❑
- ammonia ❑
- carbon dioxide ❑
- steam ❑

b) The Earth's early atmosphere mainly consisted of carbon dioxide. Name a planet in the Solar system which has an atmosphere today similar to the Earth's early atmosphere. (1 mark)

....

....

....

c) What did the steam released by the volcanoes eventually produce? (1 mark)

....

....

....

d) Why did the amount of oxygen in the atmosphere eventually increase? (1 mark)

....

....

....

e) The amount of nitrogen in the Earth's atmosphere has also increased over time. Some nitrogen was produced when ammonia reacted with oxygen. How else was nitrogen produced? (1 mark)

....

....

....

....

....

....

How well did you do? ✗ 0-9 Try again 10-14 Getting there 15-19 Good work 20-24 Excellent! ✓

Pollution of the atmosphere

A

1 Which of these elements may be found in fossil fuels? (1 mark)

a) tin ❑
b) sulphur ❑
c) gold ❑
d) silicon ❑

2 Which of these descriptions best describes the gas carbon monoxide? (1 mark)

a) green and dense ❑
b) colourless and smelly ❑
c) colourless, odourless and very poisonous ❑
d) poisonous and violet ❑

3 When fuels are burnt which of these conditions leads to the production of carbon monoxide? (1 mark)

a) insufficient supply of nitrogen ❑
b) insufficient supply of fuel ❑
c) insufficient supply of heat ❑
d) insufficient supply of oxygen ❑

4 Which of these gases is linked with 'acid rain'? (1 mark)

a) carbon monoxide ❑
b) carbon dioxide ❑
c) sulphur dioxide ❑
d) nitrogen ❑

5 Which of these events could be a consequence of global warming? (1 mark)

a) changes to the ozone layer ❑
b) icecaps could melt and cause massive flooding ❑
c) acid rain ❑
d) faulty gas appliances ❑

B

1 Complete the following passage. (7 marks)

Hydrocarbon fuels contain .... and carbon. When these fuels are burnt the gases carbon dioxide and water .... are produced and energy is released. Sometimes fuels are burnt in a poor supply of .... When this happens the gas carbon .... may also be produced. Carbon monoxide is very dangerous. It is colourless, odourless and very .... This gas .... many people every year. Faulty gas appliances are particularly dangerous so it is important that they are regularly ....

2 True or false? (5 marks)

	true	false
a) Global dimming is caused by smoke particles.	❑	❑
b) Global warming is caused by seawater rises.	❑	❑
c) Incomplete combustion of fuels produces soot.	❑	❑
d) All scientists now accept that human activity is causing the greenhouse effect.	❑	❑
e) Acid rain is caused by sulphur dioxide pollution.	❑	❑

C

1 a) **Many fuels contain carbon. Complete the equation to show what happens when carbon burns to form carbon dioxide.** (1 mark)

$C + \ldots\ldots\ldots \rightarrow CO_2$

b) **Humans are affecting the proportion of gases in the atmosphere.**

i) **How is the amount of carbon dioxide in the atmosphere changing?** (1 mark)

....

....

ii) **Why is the amount of carbon dioxide in the atmosphere changing?** (1 mark)

....

....

c) **Some fuels contain traces of sulphur. Complete the equation to show what happens when sulphur burns to form sulphur dioxide.** (1 mark)

$S + O_2 \rightarrow \ldots\ldots\ldots\ldots\ldots\ldots\ldots\ldots\ldots$

d) **Which of these environmental problems could be caused by acid rain? Tick two boxes.** (2 marks)

- damage to statues ☐
- global dimming ☐
- damage to trees ☐
- skin cancers ☐
- changes to weather patterns ☐
- increased sea levels ☐

2 **Which of these environmental problems could be caused by increased levels of smoke particles in the atmosphere? Tick one box.** (1 mark)

- damage to statues ☐
- global dimming ☐
- damage to trees ☐
- skin cancers ☐

3 a) **Name the two elements found in hydrocarbon fuels.** (2 marks)

....

....

....

....

b) **When hydrocarbon fuels are burnt, the gas carbon dioxide can be made. Which of these environmental problems could be caused by increased levels of carbon dioxide in the atmosphere? Tick one box.** (2 marks)

- damage to trees ☐
- increased sea levels ☐
- global dimming ☐
- skin cancers ☐

How well did you do? ✗ 0-11 Try again 12-16 Getting there 17-22 Good work 23-28 Excellent! ✓

Pollution of the environment

A

1 Which of these gases can be produced when PVC is burnt? (1 mark)

a) hydrogen chloride ☐
b) chlorine ☐
c) cyanide ☐
d) bromine ☐

2 Which of these substances could be described as non-biodegradable? (1 mark)

a) bananas ☐
b) leaves ☐
c) newspapers ☐
d) plastics ☐

3 Which of these issues could be an advantage of limestone quarrying in an area? (1 mark)

a) destruction of animal habitats ☐
b) new jobs ☐
c) many heavy lorries ☐
d) scarring of the landscape ☐

4 Which of these statements is true of non-biodegradable plastics? (1 mark)

a) they are reactive ☐
b) they do not rot away ☐
c) they react with water ☐
d) they react with oxygen in the air ☐

5 What is the main ore of aluminium? (1 mark)

a) aluminium sulphide ☐
b) haematite ☐
c) bauxite ☐
d) cryolite ☐

B

1 Complete each passage by crossing out the incorrect word or phrase. (5 marks)

a) Aluminium ore is extracted from large/small open cast mines.
b) Trees have to be cut down near aluminium ore mines to build airports/roads.
c) By recycling aluminium objects in this country we can increase/decrease the speed at which our tips are filled up.
d) The area around mines is improved/polluted by litter and oil.
e) Aluminium/sodium is used to make drinks cans.

2 Complete the following passages. (7 marks)

Plastics are very stable so they do not .... easily. This makes plastics very useful. Most plastics do not react with water or with .... in the air. They are also .... which means that they are not decomposed by microbes. Some plastics can be .... however; this can produce poisonous gases like ....

Scientists have recently developed a new range of .... plastics. These plastics are more easy to dispose of because they will eventually .... away.

C

1 **This question is about the extraction of limestone rock. Use the words in the box below to complete the sentences.** (4 marks)

landscape	quarries
pollution	calcium carbonate

Limestone is a type of sedimentary rock. The main chemical compound in limestone is a) .... Limestone is extracted from b) .... in large quantities. This can scar the c) .... and cause noise d) ....

2 **Aluminium can be extracted from the mineral bauxite. Bauxite is often found in environmentally sensitive areas like the Amazonian rain forest.**

a) **Suggest two ways in which a new bauxite quarry could be of benefit to people who live near to the mine.** (2 marks)

....

....

....

b) **Suggest two ways in which a new bauxite quarry could damage the local environment.** (2 marks)

....

....

....

....

3 **This question is about plastics. Use the words in the box below to complete the sentences.** (4 marks)

hydrogen chloride	oxygen
microbes	unreactive

Most plastics are very a) ....
They do not react with b) .... in the air or with living c) ....
Some plastics can be burnt. Burning plastic PVC produces d) ....

4 **Suggest why it is a good idea to recycle old drinks cans.** (1 mark)

....

....

....

How well did you do? ✗ 0-12 Try again 13-18 Getting there 19-24 Good work 25-30 Excellent! ✓

Evidence for plate tectonics

A

1 Which of these layers is found at the centre of the Earth? (1 mark)

a) outer core ☐
b) inner core ☐
c) mantle ☐
d) crust ☐

2 What does the Earth's lithosphere comprise? (1 mark)

a) mantle and outer core ☐
b) inner and outer core ☐
c) crust and upper mantle ☐
d) crust and outer core ☐

3 What is believed to cause the convection currents that drive the movement of the Earth's plates? (1 mark)

a) earthquakes ☐
b) icelandic power stations ☐
c) natural radioactive decay ☐
d) magnetism ☐

4 What do scientists believe that the Earth's core is made of? (1 mark)

a) carbon and silicon ☐
b) iron and nickel ☐
c) iron and silicon ☐
d) silicon and oxygen ☐

5 Which elements are most abundant in the Earth's crust? (1 mark)

a) silicon, iron and magnesium ☐
b) silicon, oxygen and iron ☐
c) magnesium and nickel ☐
d) silicon, aluminium and oxygen ☐

B

1 Label the diagram to show the layered structure of the Earth. (5 marks)

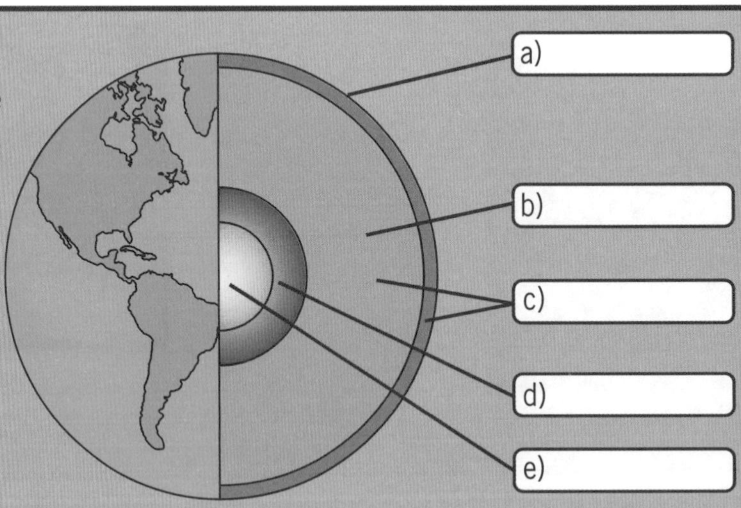

a) ______
b) ______
c) ______
d) ______
e) ______

2 True or false? (5 marks)

	true	false
a) The Earth's lithosphere is split into three plates.	☐	☐
b) Oceanic crust is mainly basalt.	☐	☐
c) The outer and inner cores are liquid.	☐	☐
d) The density of rocks increases with depth.	☐	☐
e) The Earth's mantle slowly flows.	☐	☐

Answer Booklet

GCSE Science Higher

GCSE Success

Workbook Answer Booklet

Science Higher

Brian Arnold • Elaine Gill • Emma Poole

Answers

Biology

Pages 4–5 A balanced diet and nutrition

A

1. b 2. b 3. b 4. a 5. b

B

1.

Nutrient	Found in	Used for
carbohydrate	cereals	**energy**
fibre	**plants**	moving food in gut
water	all food and drink	cools us down
protein	lean meat	**growth/repair of cells**
salt	**processed foods**	nervous impulses

2. a) suppresses the appetite, burning protein uses more calories than burning fats and carbohydrates, prevents blood sugar levels and insulin levels 'yo-yoing' causing hunger, restricts food groups you eat so restricts calories consumed
   b) kidney problems, increased cholesterol, increased risk of diabetes

C

1. a) 400 kJ
   b) Tom's tomatoes – contain less energy/carbohydrates/fats
   c) Tom's tomatoes – contain less salt
   d) more protein
2. a) 1000 kJ
   b) growing
   c) needs energy for growing embryo/foetus/baby
   d) changed into fat and glycogen and stored
   e) anorexia
   f) reduced resistance to infection; pale, papery skin; in women, irregular periods

Pages 6–7 The nervous system

A

1. b 2. c 3. c 4. d 5. b

B

1.

Stimulus	Sense	Sense organ
light	sight	eye
chemicals	**taste**	taste buds (tongue)
sound waves	hearing	**ears**
pressure/ temperature	touch	**skin**
chemical	smell	nose

2. voluntary; conscious; learned; talking; involuntary; reflex

C

1. a) longer/bigger, they are also specialized to carry out a specific function,
   Axon runs down middle carrying electrical messagers
   b) information passed across a synapse by a chemical,
   Chemical diffuses across gap,
   Chemical starts up new impulse when they reach the next neurone

2.

Stimulus
Receptor
Sensory neurone
Relay neurone
Motor neurone
Effector
Response

3. a) conditioning
   b) involved a secondary stimulus (bell),
   Pavlov rang a bell at feeding times,
   this caused the dogs to salivate

Pages 8–9 The eye

A

1. c 2. b 3. b 4. b 5. b

B

1.

Cornea	helps focus the image
Lens	a hole that allows light through (in front of the lens)
Muscular iris	the protective, white outer layer of the eye
Optic nerve	contains light sensitive cells
Pupil	controls how much light enters the eye
Retina	transparent window in the front of the eye
Sclera	receives nerve impulses from the retina and sends them to the brain

2. a) false b) true c) true

C

1. a) A – ciliary muscle
   B – suspensory ligament
   C – lens
   b) short sight; eyeball too long; rays focus too soon; in front of retina
   c)

Structure	Focussing on far objects	Focussing on far objects
ciliary muscles	**contract**	**relax**
suspensory ligament	**slackens**	pulled tight
lens	fatter and rounder	**thin and flat**

2. a)

B	D	E	A	C

3. circular, radial, smaller

Pages 10–11 The brain

A

1. b 2. d 3. a 4. d 5. d

B

1. a) stare into space, freeze, no convulsions
   b) convulsions, twitches, loss of consciousness
   c)

Disorder	Possible causes/ increases risk	Symptoms/facts
strokes	blood supply to brain or part of is stopped/ high blood pressure/ smoking	paralysis/loss of speech/numbness /loss of vision/ headache/dizziness
Parkinson's	unknown	tremors/rigidity/ difficulty walking/ poor balance
tumours	exposure to radiation/ chemicals	uncontrollable growth of cells/ puts pressure on brain/malignant, cancerous or benign

C

1. a) A cortex
   B cerebellum
   C spinal cord
   D medulla
   E pituitary gland
   b) balance B
   heart D
   c)

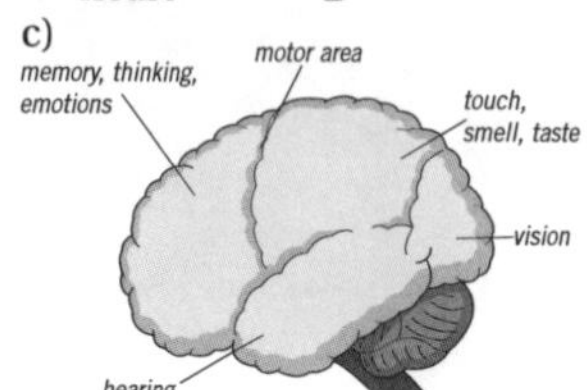

   d) outer layer of brain, divided down middle in two cerebral hemispheres, different areas have different functions
2. short – temporary storage and management of a limited amount of information
   long – the permanent storage, management and retrieval of an unlimited amount of information for later use over a lifetime

Pages 12–13 Causes of disease

A

1. c 2. d 3. a 4. c 5. c

B

1.

Feature	Bacteria	Viruses
cell wall	✓	✗
protein coat	✗	✓
respire, feed and move	✓	✗
reproduce inside living cells	✗	✓

2. a) temperature, headache, loss of appetite, sickness
   b) pathogens
3. benign – stops growing and not dangerous
   malignant – continue to grow and invade other tissues.

C

1. a) sufferers cough or sneeze, others breathe in bacteria from air
   b) antibiotics, better public health, vaccination
2.

Disease	Cause
anaemia	lack of iron
cancer	cell division out of control
red-green colour blindness	inherited
scurvy	lack of vitamin C

3. **Contact** with infected people, animals or objects used by infected people, e.g. athlete's foot, chicken pox and measles.
   Through the **air**, e.g. flu, colds and pneumonia.
   Through infected **food and drink**, e.g. cholera from infected drinking water and salmonella food poisoning.
   Unprotected sex/mixing bodily fluids e.g. HIV
4. a) cells grow out of control
   b) tumour
   c) prostate cancer
   d) low fat diet, selenium supplements to diet

Pages 14–15 Defence against disease

A

1. d 2. c 3. b 4. b 5. a

B

1. a) viruses
   b) new strains of bacteria, these bacteria resistant to current antibiotics
2. white blood cells; antitoxins lymphocytes; antibodies; phagocytes

C

1. a) barrier, produces sebum which is an antiseptic, liquid/waterproof
   b) white blood cells/phagocytes engulf/eat microbes
2. a) antigens on mumps microbe recognised as foreign,
   lymphocytes produce antibodies,
   clump microbes together,
   phagocytes engulf them,
   antibodies remain in blood
   b) dead/harmless/weakened version of disease causing microbes are injected/by vaccination, body then makes antibodies
   c) antibodies are injected
3. a) virus changes/mutates regularly
   b) virus mutates/virus damages the immune system
4. healthy humans – to see if they are safe
   diseased humans – to see if they make the person better
5. MMR
   possible side effects

Pages 16–17 Drugs

A

1. a 2. b 3. b 4. a 5. b

B

1. Drugs are powerful **chemicals**; they alter the way the body works, often without you realising it. There are **useful** drugs such as antibiotics like penicillin, but these can be dangerous if misused. Drugs affect the **brain** and **nervous system**, which in turn affects **behaviour** and risk of infection.
2. a) false b) true
   c) true

C

1. a) lowers it
   b) prevents mother's blood from carrying oxygen, deprives foetus of oxygen
2.

Drug	Organs
alcohol	1 brain 2 liver
solvents	1 liver 2 kidneys 3 heart
painkillers	1 brain

3. lung tissue is destroyed, large holes develop
4 a) nicotine
   b) carbon monoxide – prevents red blood cells from carrying oxygen
   tar – carcinogen
5. make you see and hear things that do not exist,
   gives you feelings of extreme energy,
   danger of over heating and dehydration

Pages 18–19 Hormones and diabetes

A

1. b 2. a 3. c 4. c 5. d

B

1. chemical messengers; endocrine; blood; diabetes
2. blood glucose levels, temperature, blood salt/water levels, urea levels in blood, CO_2 levels in blood
3. a) A
   b) C
   c) B
   d) D

C

1. glucose; hormones; high; insulin; liver; glycogen; normal; low; glucagon
2. a) protein
   b) urea
3. a)

Characteristic	Hormonal	Nervous
speed of action	slower	fast
lasting effect	long lasting	don't last long
where acts	may affect several organs	specific place

   b) negative feedback

Pages 20–21 The menstrual cycle

A

1. a 2. b 3. d 4. c 5. b

B

1. one mark per correct line

Change	Boys	Girls
breasts develop		✓
genitals develop	✓	✓
hair grows under the arms	✓	✓
hair grows on the face and body	✓	
menstruation begins		✓
pubic hair grows	✓	✓
sperm production begins	✓	
voice deepens	✓	

2. prepare the uterus to receive a fertilised egg,
   breaks down uterus wall when fertilisation does not occur
3. a) pituitary gland
   b) FSH – stimulates the development of the follicle (ovum)
   LH – stimulates ovulation and development of corpus luteum

C

1. a) i) C
   ii) B
   iii) A
   b) lining of uterus breaks down caused by lack of progesterone
   c) causes uterus lining to build up, stimulates egg development, stimulates ovulation
2. a) stimulate eggs to mature when female's own production is low
   b) can result in multiple egg release/births
3. maintains the uterus lining menstruation
4. taking eggs and sperm from a female and male, fertilisation outside body, implant embryo into female uterus

Pages 22–23 Genetics and variation

A

1. a 2. b 3. d 4. c 5. a

B

1. a) any two inherited features e.g. eye colour, natural hair colour
   b) any two environmental factors e.g. weight, intelligence
2. a) true b) true c) true
3.

inherited characteristic	Characteristic caused by the environment	Characteristic caused by the environment and genes
eye colour natural hair colour gender inherited disease blood group	good at sport scars speaking a foreign language	weight IQ height

C

1. a) sexual reproduction gives variation as two parents
   b) all the same colour, asexual reproduction
   c) clones
2. a) different versions of a gene
   b) Tt
   c)

Phenotype parents	homozygous tall		homozygous dwarf
Genotype	TT	x	tt
Gametes	T	x	t
F1 gen. genotype	all Tt		
F1 gen. phenotype	all tall		

   d) tall is expressed in the heterozygote
3. eye colour
   natural hair colour
   blood group
   inherited disease
4. sunlight
   soil type
   water
   temperature

Pages 24–25 Genetics

A

1. b 2. c 3. c 4. b 5. a

B

1. a) to identify all the genes in human DNA and study them
   b) Alzheimer's disease and breast cancer
   c) improved earlier diagnosis and treatment
2. plants resistant to pests, plants that can grow in adverse conditions, wheat that can take nitrogen directly from air, fruit can stay fresh for longer
3. a) forensic
   b) identify suspects, clear wrongly accused

C

1. a)

	r	r
R	Rr/rR	Rr/rR
r	rr	rr

   b) i) round
   ii) round
   iii) round
   iv) wrinkled
2. a) using genetic engineering to treat a genetic disease
   b) insert the correct gene into body cells
   c) many different body cells have the wrong gene, cells would not multiply once the gene inserted so some still have faulty gene, hard getting the DNA in cell to take up gene plus every cell in the body contains this faulty gene
3. a) an animal that carries a deliberately inserted foreign gene
   b) cow – to produce milk with low cholesterol and human antibodies
   c) designer baby/germ line therapy – IVF embryos are screened for disease or gender before implantation

Pages 26–27 Inherited diseases

A

1. c 2. b 3. c 4. c 5. c

B

1. a) CC or Cc b) cc
   c) Cc d) cc
2. a) produce large amounts of thick, sticky mucus, mucus blocks air passages and digestive tubes; difficulty breathing; difficulty in absorbing food; chest infections
   b) physiotherapy, antibiotics
   c) Explain to them that there is a one in four chance of having a child with cystic fibrosis. They then have to decide if the risk of having children is too great.

C

1. a) i) CC/Cc
   ii) Cc
   iii) person who has the allele/gene does not suffer heterozygous
   iv 1 in 4 or 25%
   v 1 in 2 or 50%
2. onset/symptoms do not show until 30–40 years old, by then person may already have children
3. a) testing a person to see if they have a genetic disease
   b) couples can make informed decisions on pregnancy/terminations
4. a) stem cells have the ability to divide and specialise into any tissue/cell
   b) funding, support, regulation
   c) moral and ethical issues involved
   d) replace tissue that has lost its function e.g. heart, treat genetic disease

Pages 28–29 Selective breeding

A

1. d 2. c 3. b 4. a 5. a

B

1. a)

How embryo transplants are done

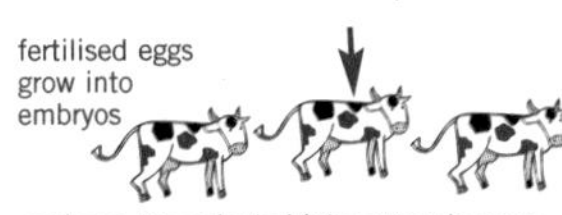

   b) sperm and eggs can be frozen and used later, many offspring can be produced by one bull or one cow
2. The nucleus was removed from an egg cell.
   The egg cell nucleus was replaced with the nucleus of an udder cell. It was then zapped with electicity so it thought it had been fertilised. This cell was then implanted into another sheep.
   The cell then grew into a clone of the sheep from which the udder cell came.

C

1.

S	P	T	Q	R

2. a) asexual
   b) all offspring will be identical, it is a quick process
3. a) they cannot cope with a change in environment and will all die, no alleles left to breed new varieties
   b) to maintain species variation
4. a) people like eating large tasty strawberries
   b) stage 1 – few cells taken from selected plant
   stage 2 – growth medium prepared
   stage 3 – cells placed in growth medium
   c) plants grown all year, plants grown quickly, plants grown cheaply, plants can be transported easily when small

Pages 30–31 Pyramids

A

1. b 2. b 3. d 4. b 5. d

B

1. a) fox
   rabbit
   grass
   b) ladybirds
   aphids
   rose bush
   c) does not tell us the size of the animals
2. a) more energy losses during production of the latter
   b) reduce number of levels in food chain, intensive farming

C

1. a) pyramid = 1
   labels correct = 3

   b) 2000 x 2 = 4000 grams
   c) lower
2. a) 100 – (75 + 15) = 10%
   b) heat
   c) urine, faeces
   d) eating

Pages 32 Evolution

A

1. a 2. b 3. b 4. c 5. d

B

1. a) competition for food, predators, disease
2. a) Organisms produce more offspring than could possibly survive.
   Population numbers remain fairly constant despite this.
   All organisms in a species show variation.
   Some of these variations are inherited.

b) there was a struggle for existence, strongest/fittest survived to reproduce
3. group of living things that can breed together to produce fertile offspring.

C

1. a) mutation
   b) easily seen
      eaten
   c) camouflaged
   d) increase in light colour
      decrease in dark colour
2. Animals die.
   The hard parts of animals that do not decay, form into a rock.
   Minerals gradually replace the softer parts of animals.
   In areas where there is no oxygen, moisture or warmth.

Pages 34–35 Adaptation and competition

A

1. c 2. a 3. b 4. a 5. b

B

1.

Definition	Word
where organism lives	habitat
all one type of animal or plant	population
living things in the habitat	community
all the living things and their physical environment	ecosystem

2. The amount of food and water available.
   Predators or grazing – who may eat the animal or plant.
   Disease.
   Climate, temperature, floods, droughts and storms.
   Competition for space, mates, light, food and water.
   Human activity, such as pollution or destruction of habitats.
   Organisms will only live and reproduce where conditions are suitable.
3. a) An animal who hunts and kills another animal.
   b) Prey is the hunted animal.

C

1. It has a thick coat to keep in body heat as well as a layer of blubber for insulation.
   Its coat is white so that it can blend into its surroundings.
   Its fur is greasy so doesn't hold water after swimming.
   A polar bear has big feet to spread its weight on snow and ice.
   It also has big sharp claws to catch fish.
   It is a good swimmer and runner to catch prey.
2. a) goes up and down, increases and decreases slightly out of synchronicity with the predator graph
   b) goes up and down, increases and decreases slightly out of synchronicity with prey graph.
   c) i) when predator population is increasing
      ii) more are being eaten
   d) i) fewer predators
      ii) less being eaten

Pages 36–37 Environmental damage 1

A

1. d 2. c 3. b 4. c 5. b

B

1. intensive; food; pesticides; fertilisers; pesticides; fertilisers; minerals
2. cause plants and algae to grow,
   plants die and decay,
   bacteria use oxygen,
   no oxygen for fish,
   fish die,
   eutrophication

C

1. a) washed into rivers/lakes/water,
      gets taken into plants,
      plants eaten by animals
   b) 5 p.p.m.
2. a) predatory mites eat the red spider mites
   b) biological
   c) only kills red spider mites/pest,
      does not harm other species,
      works over long term,
      no chemicals use
   d) predatory mite may become a pest and does not remove all of the pest population
3. a) through air,
      through water,
      through soil
   b) indicator species
   c) sludge worm,
      water louse
   d) algae
      lichen,

Pages 38–39 Environmental damage 2

A

1. b 2. c 3. b 4. b 5. c

B

1. a) true   b) false
   c) true   d) true
   e) false
2. a) extra CO_2 in the atmosphere
   b) global warming/greenhouse effect
   c) i) smaller   ii) more
      iii) UV   iv) most
      v) UV   vi) less

C

1. a) carbon dioxide, sulphur dioxide, nitrogen oxides
   b) gases dissolve in water in clouds forming acids
   c) i) dissolves the stone
      ii) makes the water acidic, kills fish/living organisms
      iii) kills them
2. a) chlorofluorocarbons
   b) aerosols, fridges, plastic foam
   c) cause a hole in the ozone layer,
      this lets more UV rays through
   d) UV rays can cause skin cancer
3. Reduce use of electricity e.g. turn lights off.
   Reduce need for cars e.g. cycle to school.
   Reduce deforestation by using recycled paper
   We can use unleaded petrol and reduce the need for cars.
   We can use catalytic converters in cars to reduce emissions of harmful gases.

Pages 40–41 Ecology and classification

A

1. b 2. c 3. d 4. c 5. b

B

1. a) kingdom
      phylum
      class
      order
      family
      genus
      species
   b) group of organisms that can breed together to produce fertile offspring
   c) binomial
   d) same name in all countries,
      common names different in different countries
   e) Homo sapiens (one mark for name, one mark for getting upper and lower case correct.)
2. fish, amphibians, reptiles, birds, mammals

C

1. a) P – beetle   Q – snail
      R – slug   S – spider
2. a) living part (animals and plants)
      called the community
      non-living part
      called the habitat
   b) woodland,
      lakes
3. a) A – quadrat
      B – pooter
      C – pitfall trap
   b) add up numbers in quadrats = 60
      average number per quadrat = 6
      quadrat = square metre
      field 10000 square metres
      number of daisies = 10 000 x 6
      equals 60 000

Chemistry

Pages 42–43 Limestone

A

1. a 2. c 3. d 4. c 5. a

B

1. a) quicklime/calcium hydroxide/carbon dioxide
   b) cement
   c) mortar
   d) slaked lime/calcium hydroxide/limewater
   e) glass
2. a) true
   b) false
   c) false
   d) true
   e) false

C

1. a) $2NaHCO_3 \rightarrow Na_2CO_3 + CO_2 + H_2O$
   b) baking powder
2. a) $CaCO_3 \rightarrow CaO + CO_2$
   b) We are using heat to break down the calcium carbonate into simpler substances.
3. a) $CaCO_3$
   b) carbon dioxide
   c) calcium oxide
   d) water
   e) calcium hydroxide

Pages 44–45 Fuels

A

1. d 2. c 3. d 4. d 5. b

B

1. a) true   b) false
   c) false   d) true
   e) false
2. a) fractional distillation
   b) bottom   c) short
   d) not useful   e) cracking

C

1. a) C_3H_8
   b) Yes, it contains carbon and hydrogen only.
   c) Heat is being used to breakdown large molecules into simpler substances.
   d) i) C_8H_{18}
      ii) ethene
      iii) polythene/plastic/polymers/ethanol

Pages 46–47 Organic families

A

1. d 2. b 3. c 4. a 5. c

B

1. a) ethene   b) propene
   c) propane   d) ethane
2. a) a and b   b) c and d
   c) a and b   d) a and b
   e) Bromine water decolourises or turns from orange/brown to colourless.

C

1. a) No, it contains hydrogen, carbon and oxygen.
   b) Yes, it has no double bonds.
   c) propane   d) alkene
   e) propene   f) alkene
   g) butene

Pages 48–49 Vegetable oils

A

1. b 2. b 3. c 4. b 5. a

B

1. a) true   b) false
   c) false   d) true
   e) true
2. a) sweeteners
   b) flavours
   c) emulsifiers
   d) E-numbers

C

1. a) seeds, nuts
   b) get fat/heart disease/raised cholesterol levels
   c) i) C=C
      ii) add bromine water
      iii) decolourises
   d) water

Pages 50–51 Plastics

A

1. b 2. b 3. d 4. c 5. a

B

1. a) molecule A
   b) methane
   c) polypropene
2. a) false   b) false
   c) false   d) true
   e) true

C

1. a) No, it does not contain hydrogen and it does contain fluorine.
   b) It has double bonds.
   c) i) add bromine water
      ii) decolourises/orange or brown to colourless
   d) ii)
   e) non-biodegradable/unreactive/do not react with water or oxygen

Pages 52–53 Ethanol

A

1. d 2. a 3. c 4. c 5. d

B

1. alcohol, properties, dissolve, low, evaporates, fuel, renewable, less, fermentation, cereals, dioxide, yeast
2. a) true b) true
   c) false d) true
   e) false

C

1. a) ethanol
   b) carbon dioxide
2. a) fermentation
   b) yeast
   c) It allows carbon dioxide to escape but prevents oxygen entering
   d) $C_2H_4 + H_2O \rightarrow C_2H_5OH$

Pages 54–55 Evolution of the atmosphere

A

1. a 2. b 3. b 4. b 5. c

B

1. c, e, a, d, b
2. a) true b) false
   c) false d) false
   e) true

C

1. a) plants
   b) carbon dioxide
   c) ozone
   d) harmful
2. a) CFCs
   b) Venus or Mars
   c) (early) oceans
   d) plants evolved
   e) living organisms like denitrifying bacteria

Pages 56–57 Pollution of the atmosphere

A

1. b 2. c 3. d 4. c 5. b

B

1. hydrogen, vapour, oxygen, monoxide, poisonous, kills, serviced
2. a) true b) false
   c) true d) false
   e) true

C

1. a) $C + O_2 \rightarrow CO_2$
   b) i) it is increasing
      ii) burning more fossil fuels
   c) $S + O_2 \rightarrow SO_2$
   d) damage to statues, damage to trees
2. global dimming
3. a) hydrogen and carbon
   b) increased sea levels

Pages 58–59 Pollution of the environment

A

1. a 2. d 3. b 4. b 5. c

B

1. a) large b) roads
   c) decrease d) polluted
   e) aluminium
2. react, oxygen, non-biodegradable, burnt, hydrogen chloride, biodegradable, rot

C

1. a) calcium carbonate
   b) quarries
   c) landscape
   d) pollution
2. a) jobs/money/better roads/better facilities
   b) trees have to be cut down for the quarry or access roads/ loss of land/oil or litter or noise
   c) pollution/destroy local plant or animal life
3. a) unreactive
   b) oxygen
   c) microbes
   d) hydrogen chloride
4. it takes less energy to recycle aluminium than to extract aluminium,
   rainforests are preserved,
   landfill sites fill more slowly

Pages 60–61 Evidence for plate tectonics

A

1. b 2. c 3. c 4. b 5. d

B

1. a) crust b) mantle
   c) lithosphere
   d) outer core
   e) inner core
2. a) false b) true
   c) false d) true
   e) true

C

1. a) crust and upper mantle
   b) jigsaw fit of coasts/similar fossil records/similar rock strata
   c) convection currents caused by natural radioactive decay
   d) a few cms per year
   e) inner core – solid, outer core – liquid
   f) crust

Pages 62–63 Consequences of plate tectonics

A

1. d 2. b 3. a 4. b 5. c

B

1. a) oceanic plate
   b) continental plate
   c) volcano
   d) fold mountains
   e) melting
2. boundaries, slide, San Andreas, plates, stuck, forces, earthquake

C

1. a) i) mantle
      ii) outer core
      iii) inner core
      iv) crust
   b) lithosphere
   c) metamorphic
   d) it is denser
   e) west coast of South America
   f) earthquake/volcano/ tsunami
   g) There are too many factors involved.

Pages 64–65 Extraction of iron

A

1. c 2. b 3. b 4. d 5. d

B

1. haematite, Fe_2O_3, silicon dioxide, limestone, furnace, slag, slag, density
2. a) false b) true
   c) false d) true
   e) false

C

1. a) limestone and coke
   b) haematite
   c) hot air/ oxygen
   d) $3CO + Fe_2O_3 \rightarrow 2Fe + 3CO_2$
   e) reduction
   f) reacts with silica impurities to form slag
   g) it is more dense.

Pages 66–67 Iron and steel

A

1. b 2. c 3. b 4. d 5. b

B

1. a) oxygen and water
   b) more
   c) non-metallic
   d) harder
   e) different sizes

2. carbon, cast, rust, brittle, drain covers etc, carbon, softer, shape, atoms, pass/slip, gates etc

C

1. a) water and oxygen
   b) Stops water and oxygen reaching the iron.
2. a) Atoms are the same size and have a regular arrangement (1 mark) and are labelled as iron atoms (1 mark).
   b) Cast iron, in cast iron the atoms are different sizes so they do not have a regular arrangement and the layers cannot pass easily over each other.
   c) alloy
   d) strong
   e) The more carbon the harder they are to shape.

Pages 68–69 Aluminium

A

1. d 2. c 3. d 4. b 5. a

B

1. a) negative ion
   b) positive electrode
   c) negative electrode
   d) positive ion
2. a) false b) true
   c) false d) true
   e) true

C

1. a) electrolysis
   b) bauxite
   c) cryolite
   d) It has a lower melting point and bauxite dissolves in molten cryolite.
   e) negative
   f) reduction
   g) positive
   h) blue section labelled
   i) graphite/carbon
   j) The oxygen that is formed there reacts with the carbon to form carbon dioxide/carbon monoxide. So the graphite electrode is eaten away.

Pages 70–71 Titanium

A

1. a 2. b 3. a 4. d 5. d

B

1. a) true b) false
   c) true d) true
   e) false
2. a) soft
   b) nickel and titanium
   c) less reactive
   d) return to their original shape
   e) more reactive

C

1. a) rutile
   b) alloy
   c) magnesium
   d) nitinol
2. high density
3. a) magnesium chloride + titanium → magnesium chloride + titanium
   b) Magnesium displaces titanium from titanium chloride.
   c) To stop the titanium metal from reacting with air/oxygen to reform titanium dioxide.

Pages 72–73 Copper

A

1. c 2. b 3. d 4. d 5. d

B

1. a) true b) false
   c) false d) false
   e) true
2. a) soft
   b) copper and zinc
   c) copper and tin
   d) unreactive
   e) return to their original shape

C

1. a) chalcopyrite
   b) alloy
   c) ore
   d) brass
2. good thermal insulator
3. a) steel
   b) solder
   c) amalgam
   d) bronze
4. a) unreactive/good thermal conductor
   b) unreactive/easy to shape
   c) good electrical conductor/easy to shape

Pages 74–75 Transition metals

A

1. b 2. d 3. c 4. d 5. b

B

1. a) true b) true
   c) false d) false
   e) true
2. a) amalgam b) steel
   c) bronze d) brass
   e) solder

C

1. low melting point
2. a) carbon
   b) It is the only non-metal which conducts electricity.
3. a) transition metals
   b) iron
   c) alloy
   d) nickel and titanium
   e) copper and zinc
4. it is strong
5. it is shiny

Pages 76–77 Noble gases

A

1. d 2. a 3. d 4. d 5. a

B

1. a) electron
   b) unreactive
   c) increase
   d) monatomic
   e) colourless
2. a) false b) true
   c) false d) false
   e) true

C

1. a) helium
   b) 0
   c) monatomic
   d) argon
2. a) shared pair of electrons/covalent bond
   b) they already have a full outer shell of electrons so they don't need to share electrons.
3. a) it has a low density
   b) helium is not flammable.

Pages 78–79 Chemical tests

A

1. d 2. a 3. c 4. b 5. c

B

1. a) carbon dioxide
 b) bubbled
 c) cloudy/milky
 d) lighted
 e) squeaky pop
 f) oxygen g) pure
 h) glowing i) relights
 j) ammonia k) damp
 l) litmus m) red
 n) blue o) gas
 p) damp q) bleached

C

1. a) fermentation
 b) i) limewater
 ii) limewater goes cloudy
2. damp, red litmus turns blue
3. damp litmus is bleached

Physics

Pages 80–81 Energy

A

1. a 2. a 3. b 4. d 5. a

B

1. (Answers in bold)

Energy in	Energy changer	Energy out
electrical	bulb	heat and light
chemical	petrol motor	**kinetic** and **heat**
electrical	electric motor	**kinetic**
kinetic	generator	**electrical**
light	plant leaf	**chemical**
sound	microphone	**electrical**
strain potential	catapult	**kinetic + gravitational P.E.**
electrical	hairdrier	**kinetic**, **heat** and **sound**
chemical	**candle**	heat and light
chemical	**animal**	kinetic, heat, chemical
electrical	**loud speaker**	sound
light	**solar cell**	electrical
electrical	**electric lift**	gravitational potential, kinetic
strain potential	**bow, clockwork spring**	kinetic

C

1. a) chemical, gravitational and strain potential energy
 b) Yes. The energy entering the bulb is equal to the energy leaving the bulb.
 c) Efficiency = 20 J/200 J x 100 = 10%
2. a) Work done = 500 N x 20 m = 10 000 J or 10 kJ
 b) gravitational potential energy
 c) Efficiency = 10 000 J/ 15 000 J x 100 = 66%

Pages 82–83 Generating electricity

A

1. c 2. c 3. d 4. b 5. a

B

1. a) Efficiency = 1500 MJ/5000 MJ x 100 = 30%; wastage = 3500 MJ
 b) Efficiency = 2000 MJ/7000 MJ x 100 = 29%; wastage = 5000 MJ
2. Coal, oil and **gas** are called fossil fuels. They are **concentrated** sources of energy. Fossil fuels are formed from plants and **animals**. They became covered with many layers of mud and earth resulting in high pressures and **high** temperatures. Over **millions** of years they changed into fossil fuels. When a fossil fuel is burnt it **releases** energy but releases the gas carbon **dioxide** into the atmosphere. This gas can cause the temperature of the Earth and its atmosphere to increase. This effect is called **the greenhouse effect**. To make fossil fuels last longer we could drive **smaller** cars and turn **down** the heating in our homes.

C

1. a) A fuel is a substance which releases energy when it is burned.
 b) Coal, oil and gas are non-renewable fuels.
 c) Wood, animal dung and methanol are renewable fuels.
2. a) chemical energy into heat
 b) heat into kinetic energy
 c) kinetic energy into electrical energy
 d) To reduce the energy lost in the wires of the National Grid during transmission from power station to home.
 e) No polluting gases are produced.
 f) Risk of nuclear explosion and leaks into the atmosphere of radioactive material. High decommissioning costs. Need to store radioactive waste securely for thousands of years.

Pages 84–85 Renewable sources of energy

A

1. c 2. c 3. a 4. a 5. a

B

1.

Advantage of using this source	Alternative source of energy	Disadvantage of using this source
Using this fuel does not add to the Greenhouse effect	GEOTHERMAL	Obstacle to water traffic
Only low level technology is needed	TIDAL	Large area of land needed for renewal of supply
Energy can be stored until needed	SOLAR	Very high initial construction costs
Useful for isolated island communities	BIOMASS	Few suitable sites
Reliable, available twice a day	WIND	Poor energy capture therefore large area needed
No pollution	HYDROELECTRIC	Possible visual and noise pollution
No pollution and no environmental problems	WAVE	Not useful where there is limited sunshine

C

1. a) kinetic energy
 b) renewable, low level technology, no atmospheric pollution
 c) possible visual and noise pollution, no wind no energy
2. a) i) the greater the intensity the greater the power
 ii) the greater the surface area the greater the power
 b) Efficiency = 800J/2 000 J x 100 = 40%
3. a) The increase in the Earth's temperature caused by more carbon dioxide being in the atmosphere.
 b) The amount of carbon dioxide released when wood is burned is equal to the amount it takes in as it grows.

Pages 86–87 Heat transfer – conduction

A

1. a 2. d 3. d 4. c 5. b

B

1. a) 0% through windows, reduced by installing double glazing
 b) 25% through gaps and cracks around doors and windows, reduced by fitting draught excludes
 c) 25% through roof, reduced by putting insulation into loft
 d) 25% through walls, reduced by having cavity wall insulation
 e) 15% through floor, reduced by fitting carpets and underlay

C

1. a) Heat will travel by conduction from the centre to the outside edge of the bars. The wax which melts first (marble falls first) is the one attached to the best conductor.
 b) Heat source in centre, same thickness of wax, same size marble, bars same length etc.
 c) The particles at the hot end of the bar vibrate more violently. They jostle their near neighbours causing them to vibrate more and become hotter. This continues along the whole length of each bar until the whole bar becomes hot.
2. a) Double glazing 25 years, loft insulation 2 years, draft excluders 4 years, cavity wall insulation 10 years.
 b) Loft insulation – the savings pay for the insulation in the shortest time.

Pages 88 Heat transfer – convection

A

1. d 2. d 3. c 4. c 5. d

B

1. a)

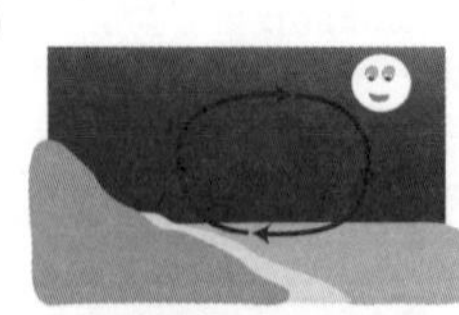

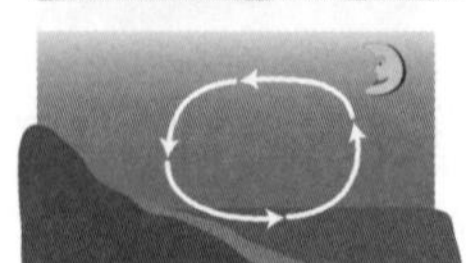

 b) During the day the land is hotter than the sea. Air above the land rises and cooler air from the sea moves in to take its place. It is an onshore breeze.
 c) During the night the sea is warmer than the land. Air above the sea rises and cooler air above the land moves out to take its place. It is now an offshore breeze.

C

1. a) Particles must be able to move position if they are to be part of a convection current. Particles in a solid have fixed positions.
 b) Air particles next to the inner wall become warm and rise. Cooler air from the outer wall moves in to take their place. A convection current is therefore set up which moves heat across the gap.
 c) If cavity wall insulation is put between the walls this stops the movement of the air particles. There is therefore no convection current and no heat loss.
2. a) As the air at the top of the fridge is cooled it becomes more dense and falls. Warmer air rises i.e. a convection current is set up which cools the whole fridge.
3. The air above the heat source becomes warm and expands. It is now less dense than the air around it and so rises. As it rises it makes the spiral turn.

Pages 90–91 Heat transfer – radiation

A

1. b 2. a 3. d 4. c 5. c

B

1. a) by radiation
 b) it is reflected
 c) it is absorbed
 d) The wax on the back of the dark sheet will melt first and its marble will fall first.
2. Heat radiation from the Sun strikes the silvery surface of the reflector. Most of the radiation is reflected towards the can. Because the can is black it absorbs most of the radiation and the water inside it becomes hot.

C

1. a)

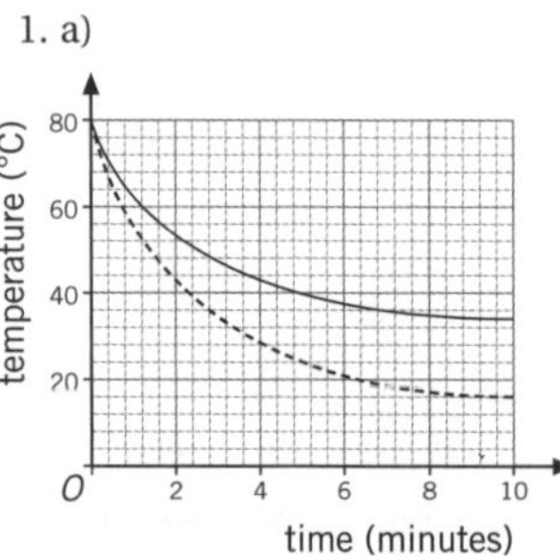

 b) The container with the light shiny surface is a poorer emitter of heat and so the water will stay warmer for longer.
 c) room temperature
2. a) Plastic is an insulator. Heat loss through the stopper by conduction is therefore very difficult.
 b) Heat is unable to escape across a vacuum by conduction or convection as there are no particles.
 c) The far side of the vacuum has a silvered surface which will reflect back any heat crossing the vacuum by radiation.

Pages 92–93 Heat transfer–warming, cooling, melting an boiling

A

1. b 2. c 3. a 4. c 5. d

B

1.

Substance	Specific heat capacity J/(kg K)	Change in temperature /°C	Mass of substance /kg	Energy lost or gained /kJ
water	4200	10	5	**210 kJ**
copper	380	**20**	10	76 kJ
iron	460	5	**60 kg**	138 kJ
lead	140	200	100 g	**2.8 kJ**
X	**400**	50	2.5 kg	50 kJ

2.

Substance	Specific latent heat	Mass of substance	Energy lost or gained
water	2.4 MJ/kg (vaporisation)	1.5 kg	**3.6 MJ**
water	340 kJ/kg (fusion)	**3.0 kg**	1.02 MJ
alcohol	**180 kJ/kg**	10 kg	1.8 MJ

C

1. a) –15°C
   b) 0°C
   c) 6 min
   d) 10 min
   e) The energy being taken in by the water is being used to break bonds in order to change its state.
   f) 1.7 MJ
   g) 2.1 MJ

Pages 94–95 Current, charge and resistance

A

1. c 2. d 3. a 4. a 5. c

B

a) i) 5 V
   ii) 4.4 V
   iii) 3.96 V
b) i) 0.25 A
   ii) 0.05 A
   iii) 0.025 A
c) i) 240 Ω
   ii) 300 Ω
   iii) 150 Ω

C

1. a) 36 J
   b) When 1 C of charge passes through the bulb 4 J of electrical energy is transferred into 4 J of heat and light energy.
   c) The p.d. across the resistor is 12 V – 4 V = 8 V. So when 2 C of charge pass through the resistor, 16 J of electrical energy is transferred into 16 J of heat energy.
2. a) and b)

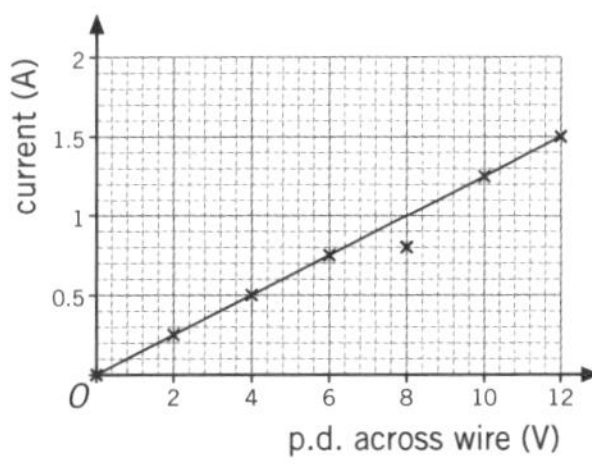

   c) 0.80 A, 8 V
   d) 8 Ω

Pages 96–97 Electrical power

A

1. b 2. c 3. d 4. c 5. a

B

1. electrical energy, forms, energy, light, sound energy (accept also heat), power, quickly, power rating, watts
2. a) The bulb is changing 60 J of electrical energy into 60 J of heat and light energy every second.
   b) 3600 J
   c) 576 000 J or 576 kJ

C

1. a) 1560 units
   b) £171.60
   c) £183.60
   d) E = P x t = 0.1 kW x 24 h = 2.4 units
   e) P = E/t = 1.8 units/0.6 h = 3 kW

Pages 98–99 Motors and generators

A

1. d 2. a 3. c 4. a 5. d

B

1. a) The needle moves a lot to the left.
   b) The needle moves a very small amount to the left.
   c) The needle does not move.
   d) The needle moves to the right.
2. wheels, knurled knob, magnet, spins, magnetic field, coil, current, coil, lights (bulbs)

C

1. a) The current in opposite sides of the loop are flowing in opposite directions. As a result one side of the loop is pushed up while the other side is pushed down. The loop therefore rotates.
   b) The wire at the top is still experiencing a force pushing it upwards and the wire at the bottom is still experiencing a force pushing it down.
   c) The split ring changes the direction of the current in the wires each time the loop reaches the vertical position, so the uppermost wire now feels a force pushing it down and the lower wire feels a force pushing it upwards.
2. a) A current which is continually changing direction.
   b) As the coil is rotated its wires cut through the magnetic field inducing a current in the wires of the coil. Because the wires are continually changing direction and cutting through the field at different rates the induced current also changes size and direction. It is an alternating current.
   c) Rotate the coil faster, use a stronger magnetic field, have more turns on the coil.

Pages 100–101 Domestic electricity

A

1. d 2. a 3. b 4. c 5. b

B

1. a) The earth wire is green and yellow and is connected to the top pin. The live wire is brown and connected to the pin on the right. The neutral wire is blue and connected to the pin on the left.
   b) fuse
   c) metal/good conductor/brass
   d) The voltage of the mains supply is much higher than that of a cells or battery and is therefore much more dangerous. It is important therefore that connections in mains circuits are made using insulated plugs.

C

1. a) If the user touches the metal casing of kettle A he may complete the circuit and current may flow through him.
   b) If the outer casing is made of plastic current can not flow through it from the heating element. So the user is safe from receiving a shock even if there is no earth wire.
   c) double insulation
2. a) If a fault develops in a circuit and too large a current passes through the fuse the wire melts making the circuit incomplete and so turning it off. The fuse therefore protects the user and limits any damage caused to the appliance by the excessively large current.
   b) i) 3 A ii) 13 A

Pages 102–103 Waves

A

1. a 2. c 3. a 4. a 5. a

B

1. A 340 m/s
   B 4 m
   C 220 Hz
   D 3 x 10^8 m/s
   E 250 m
   F 0.017 m
2. a) P-waves are longitudinal waves. S-waves are transverse waves.
   b) P-waves travel faster than S-waves.
   c) P waves can travel through solids and liquids. S-waves cannot travel through liquids.

C

1. a) earthquakes
   b) It will vibrate up and down.
   c) It will vibrate from side to side.
2. a) The core is liquid and S-waves are unable to travel through liquids.
   b) The directions change because the speeds of the waves change. The speeds change because the nature of the rocks they travel through change eg its density.
   c) Crossing boundary between different types of rock.

Pages 104–105 The electromagnetic spectrum

A

1. d 2. a 3. b 4. a 5. c

B

1. a) radio waves, microwaves, ultraviolet, infrared, X-rays, gamma rays, visible light
   b) wavelength, frequency, hospitals, bodies, cancer, precautions, screen, lead apron. Sun, tan, sun burn, sun block, glow, fluoresce

C

1. a) A – radio or television waves, B – X-ray
   b) frequency
   c) wavelength
   d) reflection, refraction, diffraction, transverse waves etc.
2. a) ageing effects, cause cancer and kill living cells
   b) sun block, covering up so little or no skin is exposed to the Sun's rays, stay indoors
   c) Water molecules inside food absorb the microwaves and become hot. The food is therefore heated throughout almost straight away. In a conventional oven the heat must travel into the food from the outside. This usually takes much longer.

Pages 106–107 Analogue and digital signals

A

1. b 2. c 3. d 4. c 5. b

B

1.

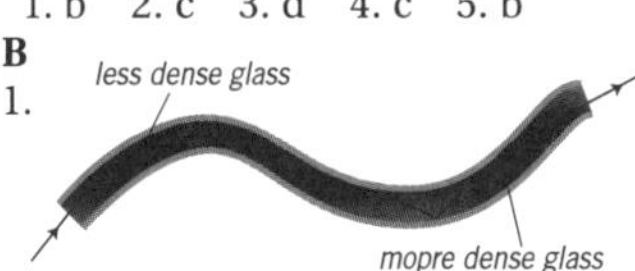

2. a) true b) false
   c) false d) true
   e) false f) true
   g) false h) false
   i) true j) true

C

1. a) Signals lose energy as they travel from transmitter to receiver.
   b) Noise is unwanted distortions added to a wave after transmission. It changes the shape of an analogue signal.
   c) It is also amplified so that the shape of the received signal may be very different from the transmitted one.
   d) i)

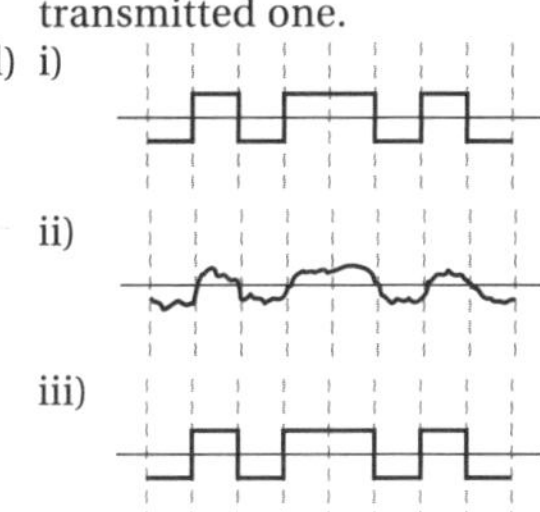

   e) The final signal is a perfect copy of the original. Digital signals can be processed by computers.

Pages 108–109 Nuclear radiation

A

1. c 2. a 3. d 4. c 5. b

B

1.

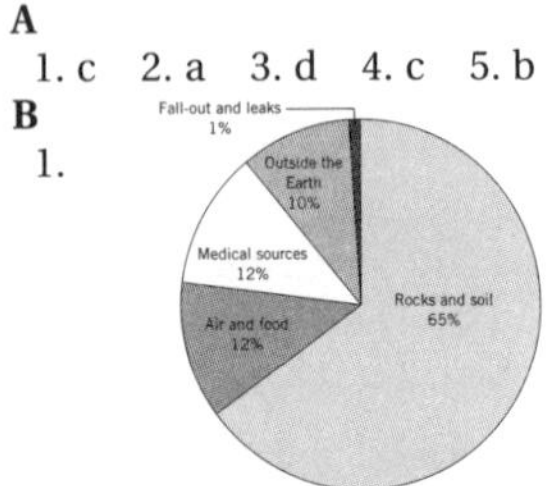

2. a) false b) true
c) false d) false
e) false f) true
g) false h) true

C

1 a) cancer, leukaemia etc.
b) Alpha radiation is the least penetrating and is unlikely to reach and damage living cells inside a body.
c) Alpha radiation is the most strongly absorbed and therefore likely to cause the most damage.
d) It is a device (usually in the form of a badge) which is used to monitor how much someone has been exposed to radiation.
e) Radiographer; someone who works in a nuclear power station or reprocessing plant or nuclear weapons establishment etc.

2. Place one source very close to a detector e.g. Geiger-Muller tube. Observe count rate. Place piece of card between source and tube. Observe count rate. If count rate has decreased this source must be emitting alpha radiation. If there is no decrease, the source is not emitting alpha radiation. Replace the card with a sheet of aluminium. Observe the count rate. If the count rate has decreased now but did not with the card this source must be emitting beta radiation. Replace the aluminium with a thin sheet of lead. If some radiation from the source is still being detected this confirms the source must be emitting gamma radiation.

Pages 110–111 Uses of radioactivity

A

1. b 2. a 3. c 4. a 5. d

B

1. alpha radiation, air particles, ions, current, smoke, ions, current, decreases, sounds
2. a) the presence and growth of bacteria
b) cool or freeze the food
c) if food is exposed to gamma radiation the bacteria are killed

C

1. a) gamma
b) The cancerous cells are killed.
c) The dose of radiation received at B and C is too small to damage/kill cells.
2. a) oil, gas
b) a leak in the pipe (possibly a blockage)
c) increase in count rate shown by detector (sudden fall in detection as tracer cannot penetrate blockage)
d) alpha and beta radiations would be unable to pass through soil/earth above pipe
e) avoids the need to dig up whole section of pipes to find leak/blockage

Pages 112–113 The Earth in space

A

1. a 2. c 3. a 4. a 5. d

B

1.

2. a) A Near Earth Object.
b) It could collide with the Earth and destroy all life.
c) Set up a program to begin to look for NEOs which might threaten Earth.

C

1. a) Large rock-like piece of ice that orbits the Sun.
b) Large piece of rock that orbits the Sun.
c) They are the remains of a destroyed planet or material which failed to form a planet.
d) The orbit of a comet takes it close to the Sun and to the far reaches of the solar system i.e. distance from the Sun varies enormously.
e) gravitational forces
f)

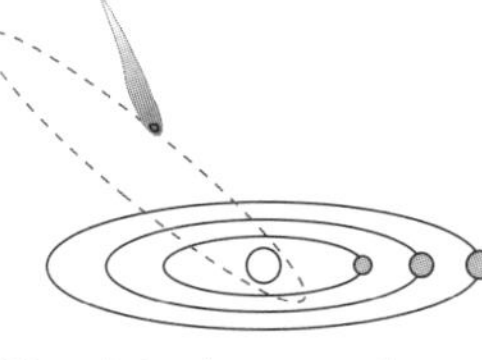

g) When it is closest to the Sun.
h) A satellite is an object which orbits a planet.
i) A natural satellite is a non man-made object orbiting a planet – for example the Moon.
An artificial satellite is a man-made object which orbits a planet – for example a weather satellite, communications satellite etc.

Pages 114–115 Stars and the universe

A

1. b 2. c 3. d 4. a 5. b

B

1. a) gases are pulled together by gravitational forces. These forces cause the gases to be compressed and their temperatures increase.
b) temperature sets off nuclear reactions.
c) large amounts of energy as heat and light. The star is formed.
d) dust and gases may gather to form planets and moons.

C

1. a) gravitational forces
b) nuclear reactions
c) energy
d) the star is in its main stable period
e) an exploding star
f) a very dense neutron star or a black hole
2. a) A theory which suggests that the universe began with all the matter in one place. This matter then exploded in all directions.
b) All the galaxies we can see are moving away from us and the further away they are the faster they are moving.
c) The Universe will continue to expand for ever or the expansion will gradually slow, stop and then reverse pulling all the matter back into one place.

Pages 116–117 Exploring space

A

1. b 2. d 3. c 4. c 5. d

B

1. a) 0.4 days
b) 250 years
c) 2.1 days
d) Mercury
e) Saturn
f) Neptune
g) Mars

C

1. a) A flyby probe investigates a planet/moon without landing. A lander lands on the surface of a moon or planet.
b) the nature of the surface i.e. mountains, craters, rivers etc.
c) soil, atmosphere, gravitational or magnetic fields etc.
d) cheaper and less hazardous
e) muscle wastage, calcium depletion
f) daily exercise, artificial gravity
g) air/oxygen supply, food and water, fuel for return journey, radiation shield

ACKNOWLEDGEMENTS

The author and publisher are grateful to the copyright holders for permission to use quoted materials and photographs.

Letts and Lonsdale
4 Grosvenor Place
London SW1X 7DL

School orders: 015395 64910
School enquiries: 015395 65921
Parent and student enquiries: 015395 64913
Email: enquiries@lettsandlonsdale.co.uk
Website: www.lettsandlonsdale.com

First published 2006

British Library Cataloguing in Publication Data. A CIP record of this book is available from the British Library.

ISBN: 9781843156680

Book concept and development: Helen Jacobs, Publishing Director

Editorial: Catherine Dakin

Series Editor: Brian Arnold

Authors: Brian Arnold, Elaine Gill and Emma Poole

Cover design: Angela English

Inside concept design: Starfish Design

Text design, layout and editorial: MCS Publishing Services

Printed in China

Letts and Lonsdale make every effort to ensure that all paper used in our books is made from wood pulp obtained from well-managed forests.

C

1 **The Earth's lithosphere is split into about twelve plates. Scientists believe that these plates are slowly moving. The diagram below shows South America and Africa. It is thought that South America and Africa were once joined together.**

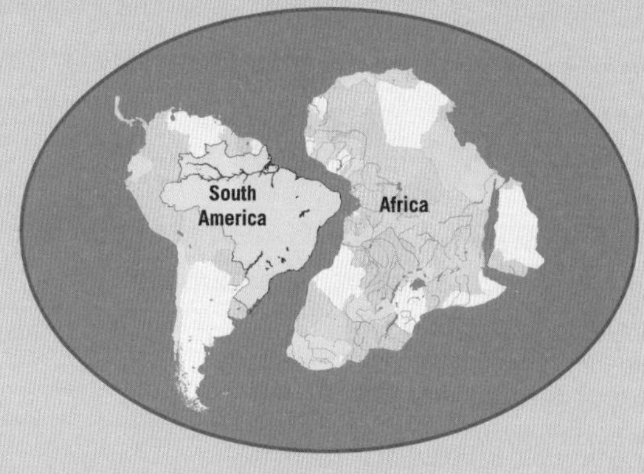

a) What is the Earth's lithosphere? **(1 mark)**

....

....

....

....

b) Give two pieces of evidence that suggest that South America and Africa could once have been joined together. **(2 marks)**

....

....

....

....

....

....

c) Why do the Earth's tectonic plates move? **(1 mark)**

....

....

....

....

d) How fast are the Earth's plates moving? Circle one answer. **(1 mark)**

a few mms per year — a few cms per year

a few ms per year — a few kms per year

e) The Earth has a layered structure. Which option best describes the state of the inner and outer core? Circle one answer. **(1 mark)**

Inner core	Outer core
solid	solid
liquid	solid
liquid	liquid
solid	liquid

f) Which layer of the Earth is mainly made of silicon, oxygen and aluminium? **(1 mark)**

- crust ☐
- mantle ☐
- outer core ☐
- inner core ☐

How well did you do? ✗ 0-8 Try again 9-12 Getting there 13-16 Good work 17-22 Excellent! ✓

Consequences of plate tectonics

A

1 Where is the San Andreas Fault? (1 mark)

a) Kansas ❑
b) Florida ❑
c) Arizona ❑
d) California ❑

2 The movement of tectonic plates causes many problems. Which of these statements is NOT true? (1 mark)

a) The problems are worst along plate boundaries. ❑
b) The problems are worst at the centre of plates. ❑
c) The problems include earthquakes. ❑
d) The problems include volcanoes. ❑

3 Where is the Andes mountain range? (1 mark)

a) West coast of South America ❑
b) East coast of South America ❑
c) West coast of Africa ❑
d) East coast of India ❑

4 What can be caused when an earthquake occurs under the ocean? (1 mark)

a) hot water ❑
b) a tsunami ❑
c) new granite rocks ❑
d) they cannot happen under water ❑

5 Oceanic plates are denser than continental plates. Which elements are abundant in oceanic rocks? (1 mark)

a) oxygen and aluminium ❑
b) iron and oxygen ❑
c) magnesium and iron ❑
d) aluminium and iron ❑

B

1 Label the diagram to show what can happen when a continental plate and an oceanic plate collide. (5 marks)

Use the labels shown in the box.

melting	fold mountains	oceanic plate
continental plate	volcano	

2 Complete the following passage. (7 marks)

Earthquakes often occur along plate .... They happen when the plates .... past each other. A famous earthquake zone is along the .... Fault in California. The .... in this area have been broken into a complicated pattern. As the plates slip past each other they often get .... together. The .... on the plates gradually build up, until eventually the plates move and the strain is released as an ....

C

1 This diagram shows the layered structure of the Earth.

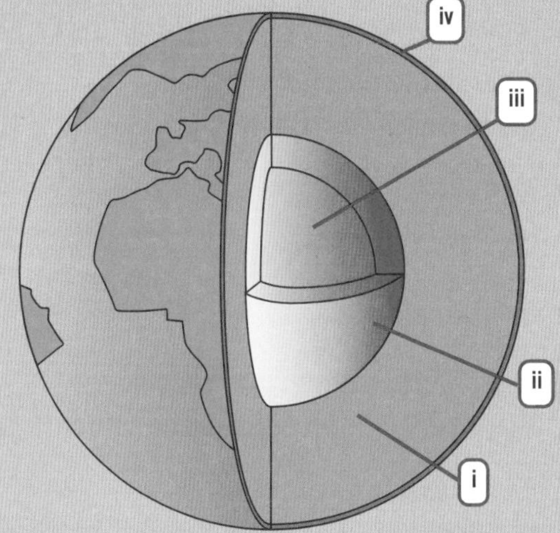

a) Add the missing labels to complete the diagram. (4 marks)

i) ....

ii) ....

iii) ....

iv) ....

b) What is the name scientists give to the crust and the upper part of the mantle? (1 mark)

....

....

c) The crust and upper mantle are split into a number of moving plates. What type of rock is formed when plates are stressed at a plate boundary? (1 mark)

....

....

d) Sometimes an oceanic plate and a continental plate collide. Why is oceanic plate forced beneath continental plate? (1 mark)

....

....

....

....

e) When oceanic plate and continental plates collide mountain ranges can be formed. Where, in the world, is this process forming mountain ranges today? Circle one answer (1 mark)

Iceland

west coast of South America

California

west coast of Africa

f) Give an example of a natural disaster which is associated with problems at plate boundaries. (1 mark)

....

....

g) Why can we not predict exactly when an earthquake will occur? (1 mark)

....

....

....

....

How well did you do? ✗ 0-10 Try again 11-16 Getting there 17-21 Good work 22-27 Excellent! ✓

Extraction of iron

A

1 **Which of these metals can be found on its own in nature?** (1 mark)

a) potassium ❑
b) iron ❑
c) gold ❑
d) calcium ❑

2 **Which of these substances is NOT a solid added to the blast furnace?** (1 mark)

a) iron ore ❑
b) carbon dioxide ❑
c) coke ❑
d) limestone ❑

3 **What is the name given to the chemical reaction in which oxygen is removed from iron oxide?** (1 mark)

a) neutralisation ❑
b) reduction ❑
c) oxidation ❑
d) endothermic ❑

4 **What is the name of the main ore of iron?** (1 mark)

a) iron sulphide ❑
b) magnetite ❑
c) galena ❑
d) haematite ❑

5 **What is the name of the substance that mainly reduces iron oxide to iron?** (1 mark)

a) carbon ❑
b) coke ❑
c) carbon dioxide ❑
d) carbon monoxide ❑

B

1 **Complete the following passage.** (8 marks)

The main ore of iron is called .... It is a form of iron oxide with the formula .... Haematite often contains some impurities. The main impurity in haematite is normally .... , which is often known as silica. When .... is added to the blast .... it reacts with the silica to form a molten substance called .... The .... has a lower .... and floats on top of the molten iron.

2 **True or false?** (5 marks)

	true	false
a) All ores contain at least 50% metal.	❑	❑
b) Coke is a good source of the element carbon.	❑	❑
c) The less reactive a metal is the harder it is to remove form its compound.	❑	❑
d) In the blast furnace carbon monoxide is oxidised to carbon dioxide.	❑	❑
e) Molten iron has a lower density so it sinks to the bottom of the blast furnace where it can be removed.	❑	❑

C

1

This diagram shows a blast furnace which is used to extract iron from iron ore.

a) Three solid raw materials are added to the blast furnace. One of the solid raw materials is iron ore. Name the other two. (2 marks)

....

....

....

b) The main chemical compound in iron ore is iron oxide. What is the main ore of iron called? (1 mark)

....

....

....

c) What is the other raw material added to the blast furnace? (1 mark)

....

....

....

d) Complete this equation to show the reaction between carbon monoxide and iron oxide. (1 mark)

$3CO + Fe_2O_3 \rightarrow 2Fe + 3$........

e) In the blast furnace iron is extracted from iron ore. Which of these words best describes what happens to the iron in iron oxide? Tick one box. (1 mark)

- electrolysis ☐
- reduction ☐
- oxidation ☐
- neutralisation ☐

f) In the blast furnace what does the limestone do? (1 mark)

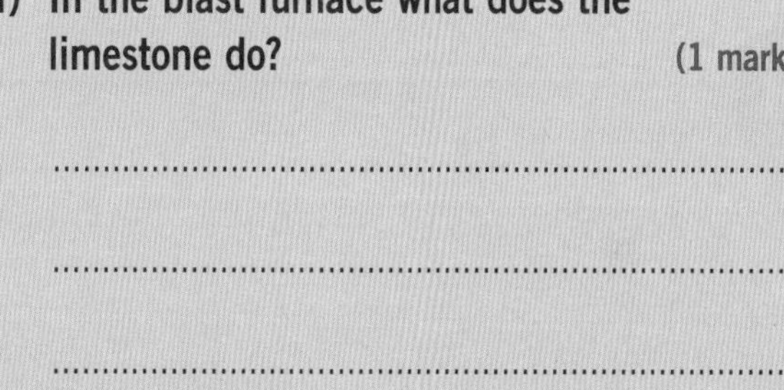

....

....

....

....

g) Why does molten iron sink to the bottom of the furnace? (1 mark)

....

....

....

How well did you do? ✗ 0-10 Try again 11-15 Getting there 16-20 Good work 21-26 Excellent! ✓

Iron and steel

A

1 Which of these metals is NOT found in stainless steel? (1 mark)

a) iron ☐
b) titanium ☐
c) chromium ☐
d) nickel ☐

2 Which of these properties is NOT true of high carbon steel? (1 mark)

a) hard ☐
b) strong ☐
c) easy to shape ☐
d) brittle ☐

3 Which of these non-metal elements can be added to iron to make steel? (1 mark)

a) sulphur ☐
b) carbon ☐
c) oxygen ☐
d) silicon ☐

4 Which of these ways would NOT stop iron from rusting? (1 mark)

a) painting ☐
b) cover in oil ☐
c) cover in plastic ☐
d) cover in water ☐

5 Roughly how much carbon is found in cast iron? (1 mark)

a) 1% ☐
b) 4% ☐
c) 10% ☐
d) 40% ☐

B

1 Complete these sentences by crossing out the incorrect word/phrase. (5 marks)

a) Coating iron in plastic stops it rusting because it stops oxygen and water/oxygen and salt reaching the iron.
b) Iron can be protected from rusting by placing it contact with a more/less reactive metal.
c) Iron can be mixed with the metallic/ non-metallic element carbon to form the alloy steel.
d) Cast iron is softer/harder than wrought iron.
e) Steel is harder than iron because it consists of atoms of different sizes/ the same size.

2 Complete the following passages. (11 marks)

Iron from the blast furnace contains high levels of the element .... If this iron is cooled down until it solidifies it forms .... iron. Cast iron is hard, strong and does not .... However, cast iron has a notable disadvantage; it is very .... Cast iron can be used to make objects like ....

Wrought iron is made by removing .... from cast iron. Wrought iron is much .... than cast iron. It is also much easier to .... In wrought iron, the iron .... form a very regular arrangement. This means that the layers of atoms are able to .... easily over each other. Wrought iron can be used to make objects like ....

C

1 a) What two substances must be present for iron to rust? (1 mark)

....

....

....

b) Explain how coating an iron fence in plastic can stop the iron from rusting. (1 mark)

....

....

....

2 This diagram shows the structure of cast iron.

silicon atoms
carbon atoms
iron atoms

a) Complete the box below to show the structure of wrought iron. Label the atoms in your diagram. (2 marks)

b) Would you expect cast iron or wrought iron to be harder? Explain your answer. (1 mark)

....

....

....

....

c) Iron can be made into steel by adding carbon and other metals such as chromium. What is a mixture of metals called? (1 mark)

....

....

....

....

d) Steel can be used to make hammers. Which of these properties should a hammer have? Tick one answer. (1 mark)

- soft ☐
- hard to shape ☐
- brittle ☐
- strong ☐

e) How does increasing the amount of carbon in steel affect how easy the steel is to shape? (1 mark)

....

....

....

....

....

How well did you do? ✗ 0-11 Try again 12-17 Getting there 18-23 Good work 24-29 Excellent! ✓

Aluminium

A

1 Why are drinks cans made from aluminium? (1 mark)

a) aluminium is not reactive ❑
b) aluminium does not react with acids ❑
c) aluminium does not react with oxygen ❑
d) aluminium reacts with oxygen to form a layer of aluminium oxide which prevents any further reaction ❑

2 What is the formula of aluminium oxide? (1 mark)

a) AlO ❑
b) AlO ❑
c) Al_2O_3 ❑
d) Al_3O_2 ❑

3 Which of these metals is the most reactive? (1 mark)

a) zinc ❑
b) iron ❑
c) copper ❑
d) aluminium ❑

4 What is the main ore of aluminium? (1 mark)

a) cryolite ❑
b) bauxite ❑
c) dolomite ❑
d) magnetite ❑

5 Why is aluminium extracted from its ore by electrolysis? (1 mark)

a) aluminium is more reactive than carbon ❑
b) aluminium is less reactive than carbon ❑
c) electrolysis is very cheap ❑
d) electrolysis is hard to spell ❑

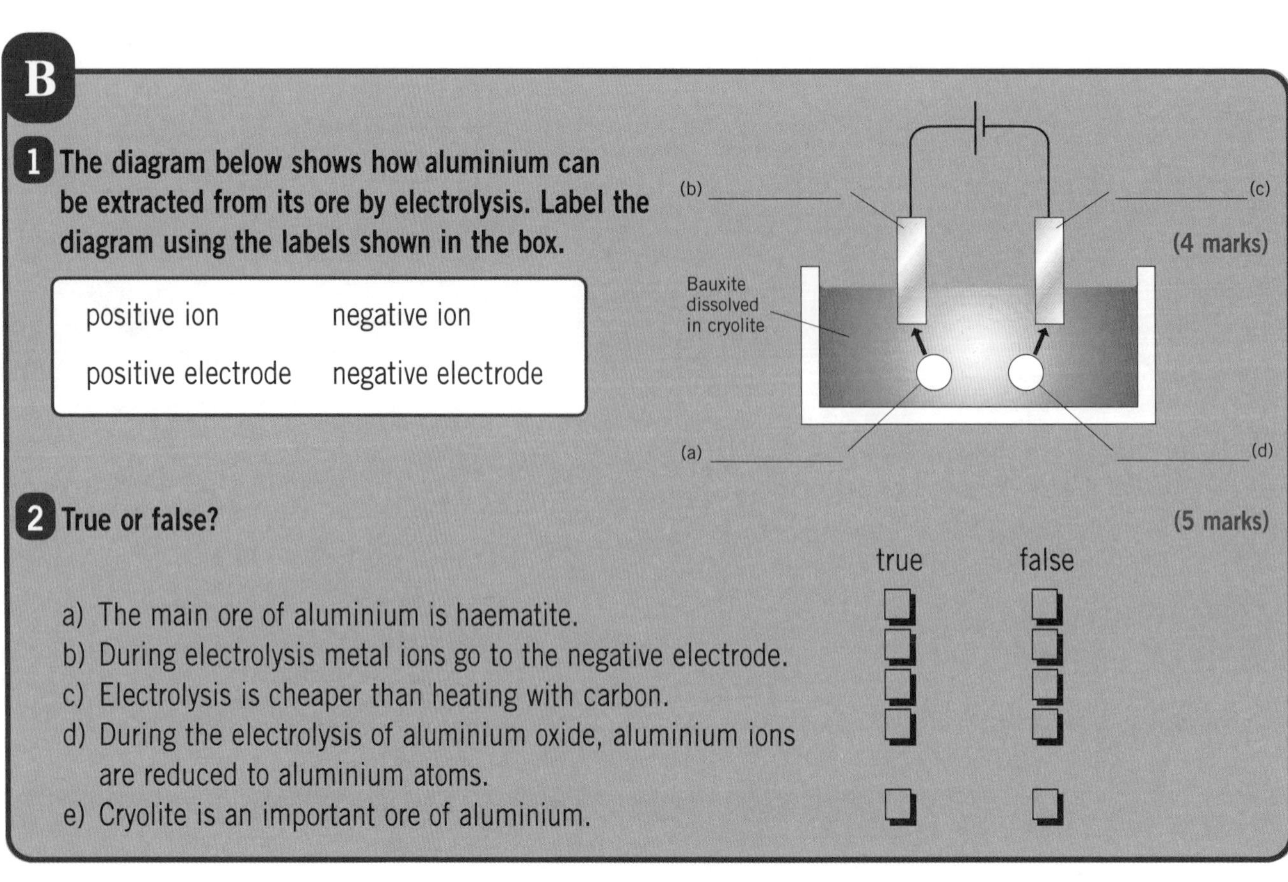

B

1 The diagram below shows how aluminium can be extracted from its ore by electrolysis. Label the diagram using the labels shown in the box. (4 marks)

positive ion	negative ion
positive electrode	negative electrode

2 True or false? (5 marks)

	true	false
a) The main ore of aluminium is haematite.	❑	❑
b) During electrolysis metal ions go to the negative electrode.	❑	❑
c) Electrolysis is cheaper than heating with carbon.	❑	❑
d) During the electrolysis of aluminium oxide, aluminium ions are reduced to aluminium atoms.	❑	❑
e) Cryolite is an important ore of aluminium.	❑	❑

C

1 This diagram shows how the metal aluminium can be extracted from aluminium oxide.

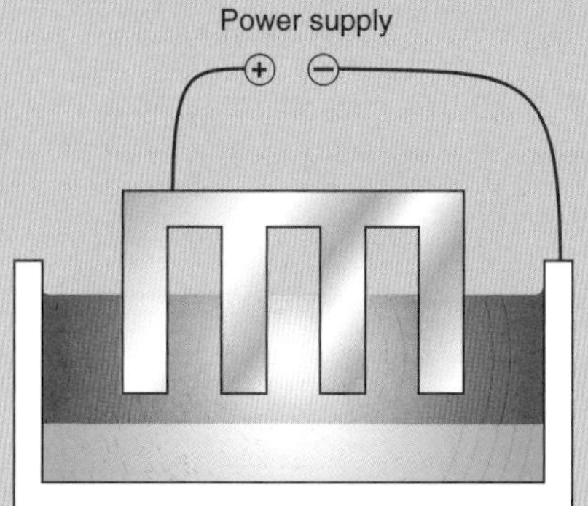

a) What is the name given to this process? (1 mark)

....

b) Name the main ore of aluminium. (1 mark)

....

c) Name the other ore of aluminium that is also used in the extraction of aluminium. (1 mark)

....

d) Why is the other ore of aluminium used? (1 mark)

....

....

....

e) During the electrolysis of aluminium oxide, the aluminium ions move. Which electrode do these ions move towards? (1 mark)

....

....

f) Which of these words best describes what happens to aluminium ions during electrolysis? Tick one box. (1 mark)

displacement ☐
reduction ☐
oxidation ☐
neutralisation ☐

g) During the electrolysis of aluminium oxide, the oxide ions also move. Which electrode do these ions move towards? (1 mark)

....

....

....

....

h) On the diagram above, label the positive electrode. (1 mark)

i) What material is the positive electrode made from? (1 mark)

....

....

....

....

j) Why must the positive electrode be periodically replaced? (1 mark)

....

....

....

....

How well did you do? ✗ 0-9 Try again 10-14 Getting there 15-19 Good work 20-24 Excellent! ✓

Titanium

A

1 Which of these metals is the most reactive? (1 mark)

a) titanium ❑
b) copper ❑
c) iron ❑
d) gold ❑

2 Titanium is a useful metal. Which of these properties does titanium NOT have? (1 mark)

a) low density ❑
b) difficult to shape ❑
c) very high melting point ❑
d) resistant to corrosion ❑

3 What is the main ore of titanium? (1 mark)

a) rutile ❑
b) haematite ❑
c) chalcopyrite ❑
d) chalcosine ❑

4 Why does titanium appear to be less reactive than its position in the reactivity series suggests? (1 mark)

a) Titanium forms a layer of titanium sulphide which prevents any further reaction. ❑
b) Titanium is very resistant to corrosion. ❑
c) Titanium forms a layer of aluminium oxide which prevents any further reaction. ❑
d) Titanium forms a layer of titanium oxide which prevents any further reaction. ❑

5 What is a mixture of metals called? (1 mark)

a) compound ❑
b) mixture ❑
c) emulsion ❑
d) alloy ❑

B

1 True or false? (5 marks)

	true	false
a) Titanium is more abundant in the Earth's crust than copper.	❑	❑
b) Titanium is less reactive than iron.	❑	❑
c) The main ore of titanium, rutile is very resistant to corrosion.	❑	❑
d) Magnesium is more reactive than titanium.	❑	❑
e) Titanium dioxide has the formula TiO.	❑	❑

2 Complete these sentences by crossing out the incorrect word/phrase (5 marks)

a) Pure titanium is too soft/hard for many uses.
b) Nitinol is an alloy of nickel and copper/nickel and titanium.
c) Titanium metals appear to be more reactive/less reactive than it really is because titanium forms a layer of titanium dioxide which prevents any further reaction.
d) When shape memory alloys are heated they change colour/ return to their original shape.
e) In the extraction of titanium from titanium dioxide the titanium is extracted by displacement by molten magnesium. Magnesium is more reactive/less reactive than titanium.

C

1 **This question is about copper and titanium metals.**

Use the words below to complete the table. **(4 marks)**

nitinol magnesium alloy rutile

Name	Description
a)	the main ore of titanium
b)	a mixture of metals
c)	the metal used to displace titanium from titanium chloride
d)	a smart alloy

2 **Titanium is a very useful metal.**

Which of these properties does titanium NOT have? Tick one box. **(1 mark)**

- high density ☐
- high melting point ☐
- easy to shape ☐
- high resistance to corrosion ☐

3 **This flow diagram shows stages in the manufacture of titanium metal from titanium oxide. In the first stage titanium oxide is converted to titanium chloride. In the second stage titanium chloride is reacted with molten magnesium.**

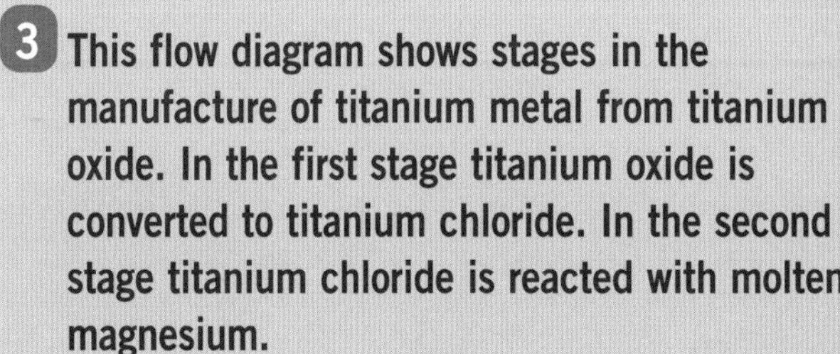

titanium oxide
↓ stage ①
titanium chloride
↓ stage ②
titanium

a) **Give the word equation for the reaction between magnesium and titanium chloride.** **(1 mark)**

....

....

....

....

....

b) **Why could this reaction be described as a displacement reaction?** **(1 mark)**

....

....

....

....

....

c) **Why must this reaction be carried out under a vacuum?** **(1 mark)**

....

....

....

....

....

How well did you do? ✗ 0-9 Try again 10-13 Getting there 14-18 Good work 19-23 Excellent! ✓

Copper

A

1 How long have people used copper? (1 mark)

a) since the mid-twentieth century ☐
b) since Roman times ☐
c) since ancient times ☐
d) since the Middle Ages ☐

2 Copper is a useful metal. Which of these applications is copper NOT used in large quantities? (1 mark)

a) water pipes ☐
b) aircraft bodies ☐
c) saucepans ☐
d) electrical wiring ☐

3 Which of these minerals is an ore of copper? (1 mark)

a) rutile ☐
b) haematite ☐
c) bauxite ☐
d) chalcosine ☐

4 Copper is a useful metal. Which of these properties does copper NOT have? (1 mark)

a) good thermal conductor ☐
b) resistant to corrosion ☐
c) unreactive ☐
d) poor electrical conductor ☐

5 What is a mixture of metals called? (1 mark)

a) compound ☐
b) mixture ☐
c) emulsion ☐
d) alloy ☐

B

1 True or false? (5 marks)

	true	false
a) Copper is a good thermal conductor.	☐	☐
b) There are concerns that cooking acidic foods like rhubarb in copper saucepans could cause long-term health problems.	☐	☐
c) Copper is purified by filtering the hot metal to remove impurities.	☐	☐
d) Gold is more reactive than copper.	☐	☐
e) When copper is extracted from copper oxide the copper is reduced.	☐	☐

2 Complete these sentences by crossing out the incorrect word/phrase. (5 marks)

a) Pure copper is too soft/hard for many uses.
b) Brass is an alloy of copper and zinc/tin.
c) Bronze is an alloy of copper and zinc/tin.
d) Copper is a very reactive/unreactive metal.
e) When shape memory alloys are heated they change colour/ return to their original shape.

C

1 **This question is about copper.**

Use the words below to complete the table. (4 marks)

ore

chalcopyrite

alloy

brass

Name	Description
a)	an ore of copper
b)	a mixture of metals
c)	a mineral which contains metal
d)	made from copper and zinc

2 **Copper is a very useful metal.**

Which of these properties does copper NOT have? Tick one box (1 mark)

good thermal insulator ❑

good electrical conductor ❑

easy to shape ❑

high resistance to corrosion ❑

3 **This question is about alloys.**

Use the words below to complete the table. (4 marks)

bronze

steel

solder

amalgam

Name	Description
a)	is made from iron
b)	is made from lead and tin
c)	contains mercury
d)	made from copper and tin

4 **Copper is a very useful metal. It can be used to make objects like saucepans, water pipes and electrical wires.** (1 mark)

a) Why is copper used to make saucepans? (1 mark)

....

b) Why is copper used to make water pipes? (1 mark)

....

c) Why is copper used to make electrical wires? (1 mark)

....

How well did you do? ✗ 0-11 Try again 12-16 Getting there 17-22 Good work 23-28 Excellent! ✓

Transition metals

A

1 Which of these transition metals rusts? (1 mark)

a) copper ❑
b) iron ❑
c) nickel ❑
d) platinum ❑

2 Which of these properties do you NOT expect of a metal? (1 mark)

a) good electrical conductor ❑
b) good thermal conductor ❑
c) can be hammered into shape ❑
d) brittle ❑

3 Which of these properties do you NOT expect of a transition metal? (1 mark)

a) hard ❑
b) strong ❑
c) forms white compounds ❑
d) tough ❑

4 What is a mixture of metals called? (1 mark)

a) emulsion ❑
b) compound ❑
c) oxide ❑
d) alloy ❑

5 Which of these examples is NOT a common alloy? (1 mark)

a) steel ❑
b) iron ❑
c) brass ❑
d) amalgam ❑

B

1 True or false? (5 marks)

	true	false
a) A catalyst increases the rate of a chemical reaction.	❑	❑
b) Transition metals are often good catalysts.	❑	❑
c) Transition metals form white compounds which dissolve to give colourless solutions.	❑	❑
d) Copper is used in the Haber process.	❑	❑
e) Nickel is used in the manufacture of margarine.	❑	❑

2 Complete the table to show the names of some common alloys. (5 marks)

Name of alloy	What is the alloy made of?
a)	mainly mercury
b)	iron, carbon and other metals like chromium
c)	copper and tin
d)	copper and zinc
e)	lead and tin

C

1 **Which of these properties is NOT typical of a transition metal? Tick one box.** (1 mark)

hard wearing ❑
good thermal conductor ❑
strong ❑
low melting point ❑

2 **Graphite is a form of the non-metal element carbon. It is dark grey solid substance which is soft, brittle and conducts electricity.**

Which property of graphite makes it an exceptional non-metal? (1 mark)

....
....
....
....

3 **The diagram below shows a section of the periodic table.**

'middle block'
Sc Ti V Cr Mn Fe Co Ni Cu Zn

a) What is the name given to the area of the periodic table described in the diagram as the 'middle block'? (1 mark)

....
....

b) What is the name of the element which has the symbol Fe? (1 mark)

....
....

c) What is the name given to a mixture of different metals? (1 mark)

....
....
....

d) Which two metals shown in the diagram are used to make nitinol? (1 mark)

....
....
....

e) Which two metals shown in the diagram are used to make brass? (1 mark)

....
....
....

4 **Which of these properties makes iron a good metal to make cars from? Tick one box.** (1 mark)

it rusts ❑
it is heavy ❑
it is strong ❑

5 **Which of these properties makes nickel a good metal to make coins from? Tick one box.** (1 mark)

it is shiny ❑
it is a good catalyst ❑
it is good electrical conductor ❑

How well did you do? ✗ 0-9 Try again 10-14 Getting there 15-19 Good work 20-24 Excellent! ✓

Noble gases

A

1 What is the most unreactive group in the periodic table? (1 mark)

a) Group 1 ❑
b) Group 2 ❑
c) Group 7 ❑
d) Group 0 ❑

2 What does monatomic mean? (1 mark)

a) individual atoms ❑
b) one colour ❑
c) one outer electron ❑
d) they are colourless ❑

3 How many electrons do noble gas atoms have to gain to get a full outer shell? (1 mark)

a) 1 ❑
b) 2 ❑
c) 7 ❑
d) 0 ❑

4 Which noble gas is used in light bulbs? (1 mark)

a) helium ❑
b) neon ❑
c) krypton ❑
d) argon ❑

5 Which noble gas is used in air balloons? (1 mark)

a) helium ❑
b) neon ❑
c) krypton ❑
d) argon ❑

B

1 Complete the following sentences by crossing out the incorrect word/phrase. (5 marks)

a) The noble gases all have a full electron/proton shell.
b) Noble gases are very reactive/unreactive.
c) The density of noble gases increases/decreases down the group.
d) Noble gases are monatomic/diatomic.
e) Noble gases are pastel coloured/colourless.

2 True of false? (5 marks)

	true	false
a) Noble gases have no practical uses.	❑	❑
b) Noble gases already have a full and stable outer shell of electrons.	❑	❑
c) Pairs of noble gas atoms join together to form molecules such as He_2.	❑	❑
d) The noble gases range in colour from pale blue to pale pink.	❑	❑
e) Down the group the noble gas atoms get larger.	❑	❑

C

1 This question is about noble gases.

Use the words below to complete the table. (4 marks)

argon
monatomic
helium
0

Name	Description
a)	used in balloons
b)	the group of the periodic table where the noble gases are found
c)	single atoms
d)	used in filament light bulbs

This diagram shows a helium atom.

b) Why don't helium atoms join together to form helium molecules? (1 mark)

....

....

....

2 This diagram shows how two atoms can join together to form a hydrogen molecule.

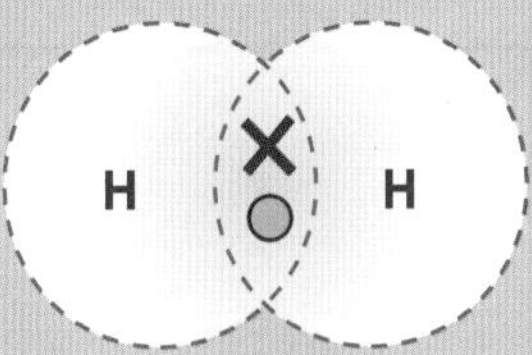

The dots and crosses represent electrons. In the first electron shell there is room for up to two electrons.

a) How are the two hydrogen atoms held together? (1 mark)

....

....

....

....

3 Helium is used in balloons.

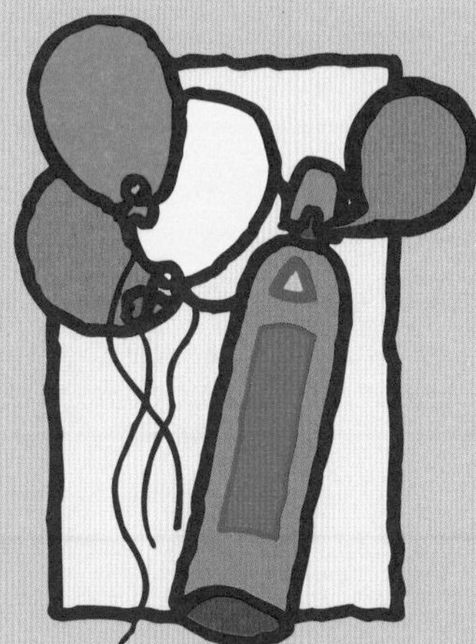

a) Why do we use helium in party balloons? (1 mark)

....

....

....

b) Why is it better to use helium than hydrogen in party balloons? (1 mark)

....

....

....

How well did you do? ✗ 0-9 Try again 10-13 Getting there 14-18 Good work 19-23 Excellent! ✓

Chemical tests

A

1 Which gas bleaches damp litmus? (1 mark)

a) oxygen ☐
b) carbon dioxide ☐
c) hydrogen ☐
d) chlorine ☐

2 Which gas relights a glowing splint? (1 mark)

a) oxygen ☐
b) carbon dioxide ☐
c) ammonia ☐
d) chlorine ☐

3 Which gas burns with a squeaky pop? (1 mark)

a) oxygen ☐
b) carbon dioxide ☐
c) hydrogen ☐
d) chlorine ☐

4 Which gas turns limewater cloudy? (1 mark)

a) oxygen ☐
b) carbon dioxide ☐
c) hydrogen ☐
d) chlorine ☐

5 Which gas turns damp red litmus paper blue? (1 mark)

a) oxygen ☐
b) carbon dioxide ☐
c) ammonia ☐
d) chlorine ☐

B

1 Complete the following sentences. (17 marks)

Gas tests

Limewater is used to test for the gas a) .... The gas is b) .... through limewater. If the limewater turns c) .... the gas is carbon dioxide.

The gas hydrogen is tested for using a d) .... splint. If hydrogen is present it will burn with a e) ....

The gas f) .... is needed for things to burn. Things burn more brightly in g) .... oxygen than they do in air. If a h) .... splint is placed in a test tube containing oxygen, the splint i) ....

The gas j) .... is tested for using k) .... , red l) .... paper. If ammonia is present the litmus paper changes colour from m) .... to n) ....

The o) .... chlorine is tested for using p) .... litmus paper. If chlorine is present the litmus paper is q) ....

C

1 This diagram shows the equipment that is used to turn sugar into alcohol and carbon dioxide.

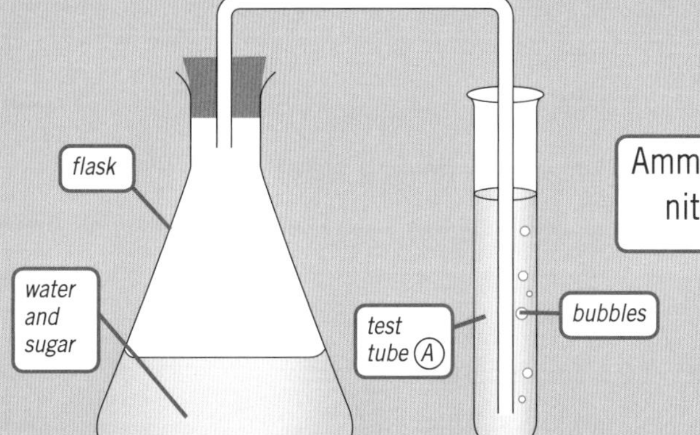

a) What is the name of this chemical reaction? (1 mark)

....

....

....

b) i) What should be added to test tube A to test that carbon dioxide has been made? (1 mark)

....

....

....

ii) What would you expect to see to solution in test tube A if carbon dioxide is being made? (1 mark)

....

....

....

2 The reaction between ammonium nitrate and sodium hydroxide produces sodium nitrate, ammonia and water.

This reaction can be summarised by the word equation

Ammonium nitrate + sodium hydroxide → sodium nitrate + ammonia + water

a) How could you tell that ammonia gas has been made?

What would you do and what would you expect to see? (2 marks)

....

....

....

3 A student carries out an experiment on an unknown compound. The compound is a bright pink colour. This means that the compound contains the transition metal cobalt. The student believes that the compound could be cobalt chloride. When cobalt chloride is heated

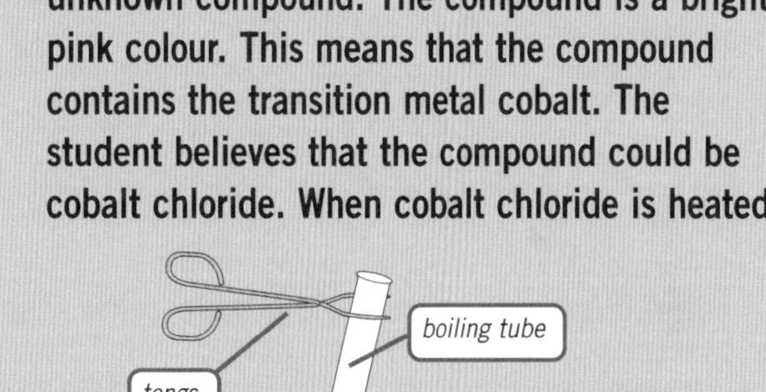

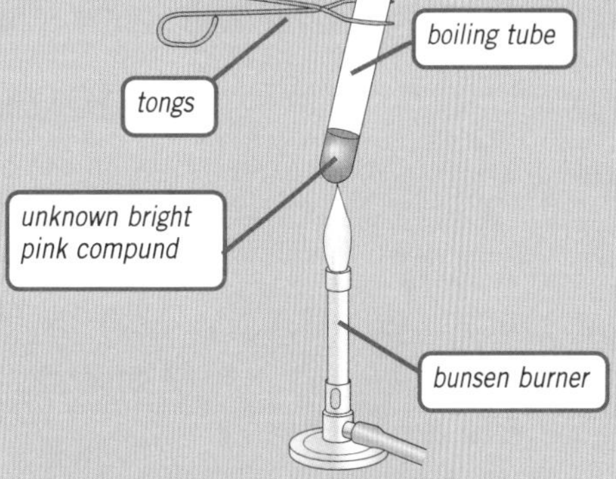

fiercely, it gives off the gas chlorine. Explain how the student should test the gas given off when the compound is heated to see if it is chlorine. (2 marks)

....

....

How well did you do? ✗ 0-11 Try again 12-17 Getting there 18-23 Good work 24-29 Excellent! ✓

Energy

A

1 **Which of the following is not a form of energy?** (1 mark)

a) power ☑
b) electrical ☐
c) chemical ☐
d) sound ☐

2 **Which of the following forms of energy cannot be stored?** (1 mark)

a) sound ☐
b) chemical ☐
c) strain potential energy ☐
d) gravitational potential energy ☐

3 **What device could be used to change to change electrical energy into sound energy?** (1 mark)

a) microphone ☐
b) radio ☐
c) megaphone ☐
d) larynx ☐

4 **As water falls down a water fall it gains** (1 mark)

a) chemical energy ☐
b) potential energy ☐
c) strain energy ☐
d) kinetic energy ☐

5 **A light bulb changes 400 J of electrical energy into 100 J of light energy. The efficiency of the light bulb is** (1 mark)

a) 25% ☐
b) 40% ☐
c) 75% ☐
d) 80% ☐

B

1 **Fill in the empty spaces in the table below. The first one has been done for you.** (20 marks)

Energy in	Energy changer	Energy out
electrical	bulb	heat and light
	petrol motor	
	electric motor	
	generator	
	plant leaf	
	microphone	
	catapult	
	hairdryer	
chemical		heat and light
chemical		kinetic, heat, chemical
electrical		sound
light		electrical
electrical		gravitational potential
strain potential		kinetic

C

1 a) Name 3 forms of energy that can be stored. (3 marks)

....

....

....

The diagram below shows the energy changes that take place in a bulb

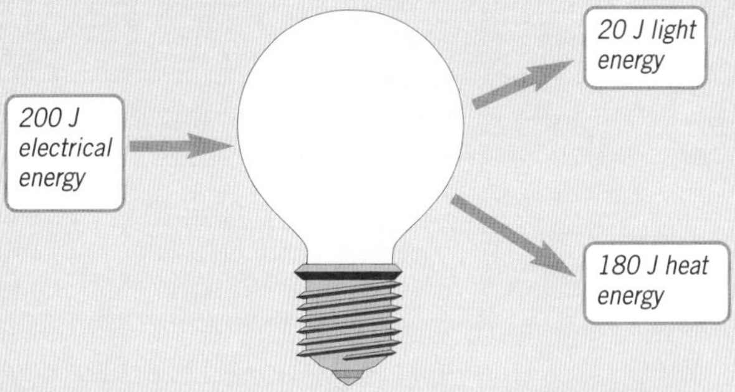

b) Are the energy values shown in the above diagram consistent with the Law of Conservation of Energy?
Explain your answer. (2 marks)

....

....

....

c) Assuming that the useful energy required from the bulb is light energy calculate the efficiency of the bulb. (3 marks)

....

....

....

....

....

2 The crane below lifts a weight of 500 N through a distance of 20 m

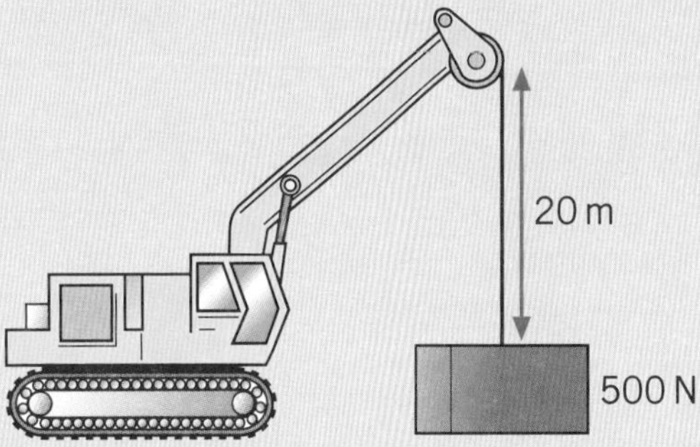

a) Calculate the work done by the crane (work done = force x distance moved). (2 marks)

....

....

....

b) What kind of energy is gained by the weight? (1 mark)

....

....

c) If the motor does 15000 J of work in lifting the weight calculate the efficiency of the crane. (3 marks)

....

....

....

....

....

....

How well did you do? ✗ 0-15 Try again 16-23 Getting there 24-31 Good work 32-39 Excellent! ✓

Generating electricity

A

1 Which of the following is not a fossil fuel? (1 mark)

a) oil ☐
b) gas ☐
c) wood ☑
d) coal ☐

2 Which of the following is not a problem created by burning fossil fuels? (1 mark)

a) greenhouse effect ☐
b) acid rain ☐
c) deforestation ☑
d) increase in carbon dioxide in atmosphere ☐

3 Which of the following is not a solution to the rapid depletion of fossil fuels? (1 mark)

a) use alternative sources of energy ☐
b) develop more efficient car engines ☐
c) improve home insulation ☐
d) use private transport ☐

4 The energy contained in a fuel can be released by (1 mark)

a) electrolysis ☐
b) burning ☐
c) photosynthesis ☐
d) electroplating ☐

5 In a power station the kinetic energy of the turbines is changed into (1 mark)

a) electrical energy ☐
b) chemical energy ☐
c) potential energy ☐
d) heat ☐

B

1 In each of the following examples calculate the efficiency of the power station and the amount of energy wasted.

a) When gas is burned at a power station 5000 MJ of energy is released. 1500 MJ of this energy is transferred into electricity energy. (2 marks)

....

b) When 7000 MJ of energy is taken from the core of a nuclear reactor it is transferred into 2000 MJ of electrical energy. (2 marks)

....

2 The following account of fossil fuels contains lots of errors. Re-write the account correcting any errors you find. (10 marks)

Coal, oil and wood are called fossil fuels. They are dilute sources of energy. Fossil fuels are formed from plants and rocks. They became covered with many layers of mud and earth resulting in high pressures and low temperatures. Over thousands of years they changed into fossil fuels.
When a fossil fuel is burnt it takes in energy but releases the gas carbon monoxide into the atmosphere. This gas can cause the temperature of the Earth and its atmosphere to increase. This effect is called acid rain. To make fossil fuels last longer we could drive bigger cars and turn up the heating in our homes.

C

1 a) What is a fuel? (1 mark)

....

....

....

b) Name two non renewable fuels. (2 marks)

....

....

....

c) Name one renewable fuel. (1 mark)

....

....

....

2 The diagram below shows the main features of a gas power station.

a) Describe the energy change that takes place in the boiler. (1 mark)

....

....

....

b) Describe the energy change that takes place in the turbine section (1 mark)

....

....

....

c) Describe the energy change that takes place in the generator section. (1 mark)

....

....

....

d) Why does the electrical energy produced by the generator pass through a transformer before going into the National Grid? (3 marks)

....

....

....

e) Give one advantage of generating electricity using a nuclear power station instead of a gas power station. (1 mark)

....

f) Give 3 disadvantages of generating electricity using a nuclear power station. (3 marks)

....

....

....

....

....

How well did you do? ✗ 0-13 Try again 14-19 Getting there 20-26 Good work 27-33 Excellent! ✓

Renewable sources of energy

A

1 **Which of these alternative sources of energy is not dependent on the weather?** (1 mark)

a) wind ☐
b) solar ☐
c) geothermal ☐
d) hydroelectric ☐

2 **Which of the following is not an advantage of using solar cells to produce electricity?** (1 mark)

a) no need for fuel ☐
b) no polluting waste ☐
c) constant supply of energy ☐
d) low maintenance ☐

3 **Which of the following statements about wind turbines is untrue?** (1 mark)

a) no visual pollution ☐
b) no polluting waste ☐
c) energy supply may be intermittent ☐
d) transfer the KE of the air into electricity ☐

4 **The source of energy in a geothermal power station is** (1 mark)

a) radioactive decay ☐
b) fossil fuels ☐
c) wood ☐
d) solar ☐

5 **Which of the following alternative sources of energy requires only low level technology and could therefore be used in developing countries or isolated communities?** (1 mark)

a) biomass ☐
b) geothermal ☐
c) hydroelectricity ☐
d) solar ☐

B

1 **Draw a line from each of the seven alternative sources of energy a) to a box containing an advantage of using this source and b) to a box containing a disadvantage.** (14 marks)

Advantage of using this source	Alternative source of energy	Disadvantage of using this source
using this fuel does not add to the greenhouse effect	GEOTHERMAL	obstacle to water traffic
only low level technology is needed	TIDAL	large area of land needed for renewal of supply
energy can be stored until needed	SOLAR	very high initial construction costs
useful for isolated island communities	BIOMASS	few suitable sites
reliable, available twice a day	WIND	poor energy capture therefore large area needed
no pollution	HYDROELECTRIC	possible visual and noise pollution
no pollution and no environmental problems	WAVE	not useful where there is limited sunshine

1 The diagram below shows a wind turbine.

a) What kind of energy does wind have? (1 mark)

....

....

b) Name two advantages of using wind turbines to generate electricity. (2 marks)

....

....

....

....

....

c) Name two disadvantages of using wind turbines to generate electricity (2 marks)

....

....

....

....

....

2 The diagram below shows solar cells being used to provide electricity.

a) How will the power of the cells be affected by i) the intensity of the light falling upon it and ii) the surface area exposed to the light. (2 marks)

i) ....

ii) ....

b) When 2000 J of light energy fall on solar cells 800 J of electrical energy is produced. Calculate the efficiency of the energy transfer. (2 marks)

....

....

3 Burning fuels such as coal and oil increases the amount of carbon dioxide in the atmosphere and so increases the greenhouse effect.

a) What is the greenhouse effect? (1 mark)

....

b) Explain in your own words why burning a renewable biomass fuel such as wood does not add to the greenhouse effect. (3 marks)

....

....

....

How well did you do? ✗ 0-12 Try again 13-19 Getting there 20-25 Good work 26-32 Excellent! ✓

Heat transfer – conduction

A

1 Heat will flow (1 mark)

a) from hot places to cold places ☐
b) from cold places to hot places ☐
c) quickly through an insulator ☐
d) slowly through a conductor ☐

2 A good example of a household object which is likely to be made from a good conductor and a good insulator is (1 mark)

a) oven glove ☐
b) plastic ladle ☐
c) table mat ☐
d) frying pan ☐

3 The transfer of heat by conduction cannot take place through a (1 mark)

a) solid ☐
b) liquid ☐
c) gas ☐
d) vacuum ☐

4 Carpets are good insulators because

a) they are close to the ground ☐
b) they are always flat ☐
c) they contain lots of air ☐
d) they do not absorb the cold ☐

5 Which of the following would not reduce the heat loss from a house? (1 mark)

a) installing double glazing ☐
b) turning up the thermostat on the central heating ☐
c) putting insulation in the loft ☐
d) fitting draught excluders ☐

B

1 The diagram below shows how heat is lost from an un-insulated home. Unfortunately the words and numbers for all 5 labels have become mixed up. Using only the words given below write out the correct labels in the correct positions around the house. Each word and number should be used only once. (10 marks)

reduced by	insulation	through floor	and cracks	25%	wall
reduced by	through walls	and underlay	through	15%	insulation
reduced by	having cavity	fitting draft	excluders	25%	
reduced by	and windows	through gaps	installing	putting	
reduced by	into loft	double glazing	10%	windows	
roof	fitting carpets	around doors	25%	through	

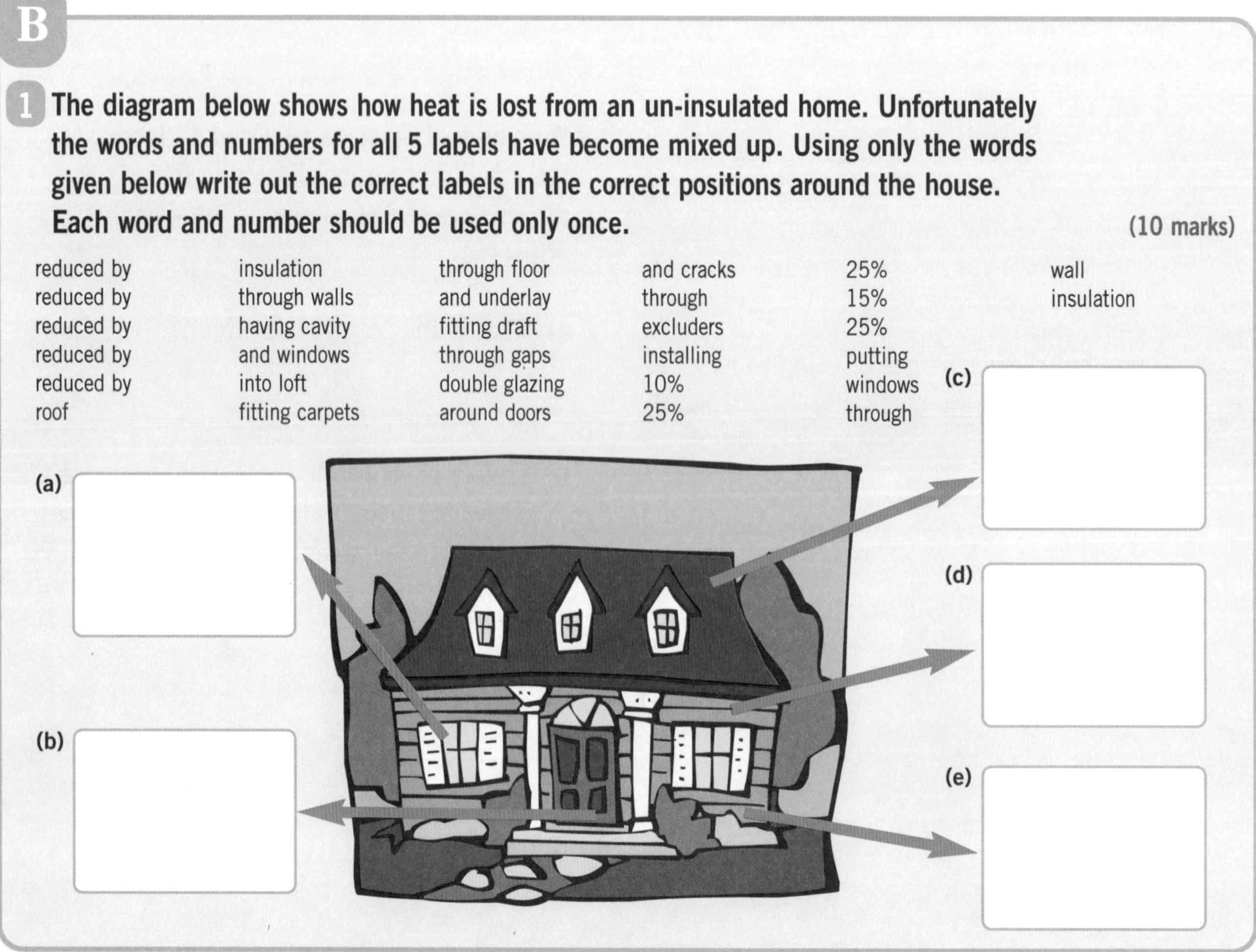

C

1 The diagram to the right shows a piece of apparatus used to compare the conductivities of different metals.

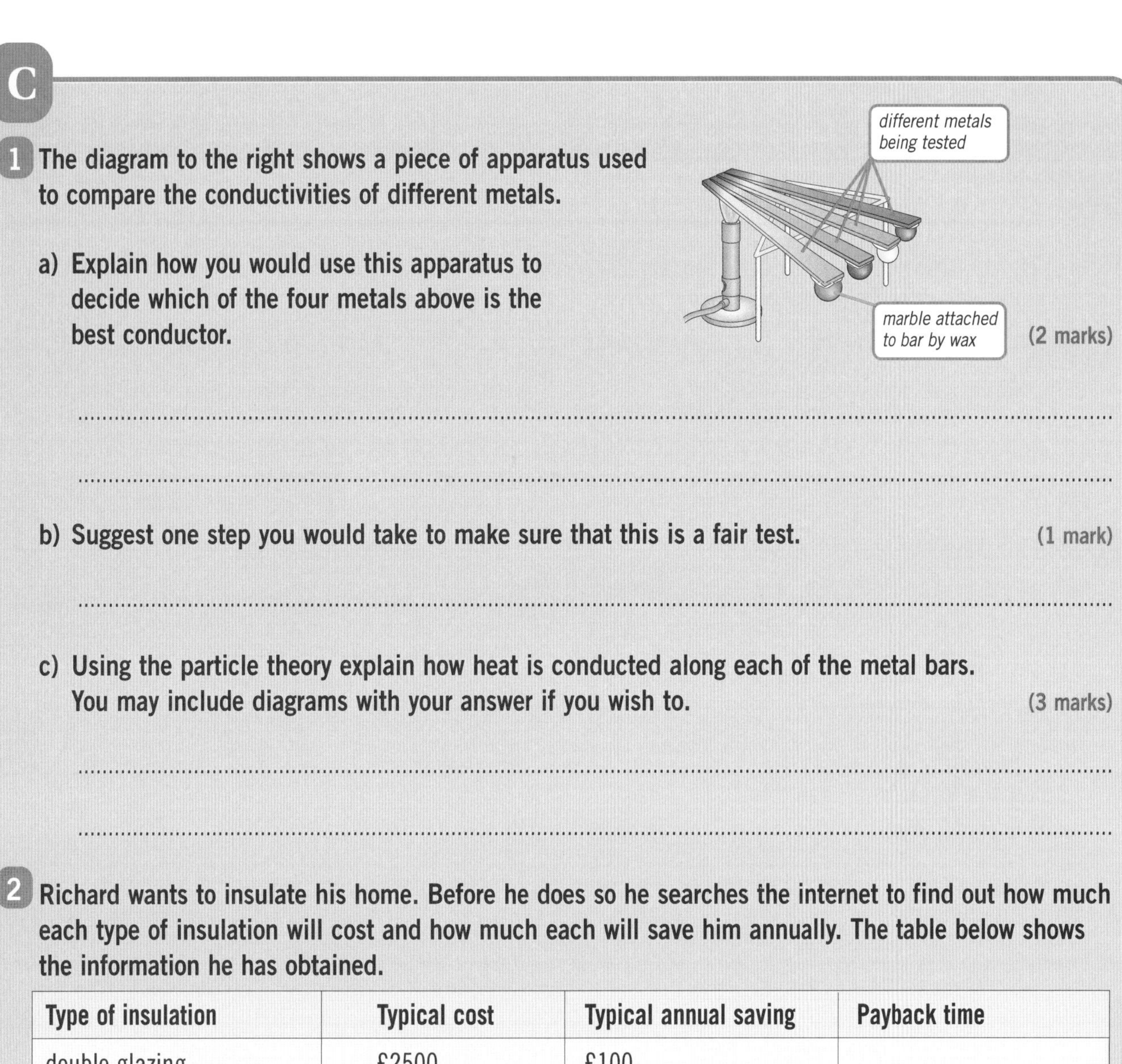

a) Explain how you would use this apparatus to decide which of the four metals above is the best conductor. (2 marks)

....

....

b) Suggest one step you would take to make sure that this is a fair test. (1 mark)

....

c) Using the particle theory explain how heat is conducted along each of the metal bars. You may include diagrams with your answer if you wish to. (3 marks)

....

....

2 Richard wants to insulate his home. Before he does so he searches the internet to find out how much each type of insulation will cost and how much each will save him annually. The table below shows the information he has obtained.

Type of insulation	Typical cost	Typical annual saving	Payback time
double glazing	£2500	£100	
loft insulation	£200	£100	
draft excluders	£100	£25	
cavity wall insulation	£500	£50	

a) Work out the payback time for each type of insulation. Write each of your answers in the correct space in the table. (4 marks)

....

....

....

b) Which type of insulation is most cost effective? Explain your answer. (2 marks)

....

....

How well did you do? ✗ 0-10 Try again 11-16 Getting there 17-21 Good work 22-27 Excellent! ✓

Heat transfer – convection

A

1 In which kinds of materials can convection not take place? (1 mark)

a) gases ❑
b) liquids ❑
c) fluids ❑
d) solids ❑

2 The circular movement of air caused by heat is called (1 mark)

a) transpiration ❑
b) evaporation ❑
c) radiation ❑
d) a convection current ❑

3 To heat the whole of an oven its burners should be (1 mark)

a) at the top ❑
b) in the middle ❑
c) at the bottom ❑
d) at the top and the bottom ❑

4 When air is warmed it becomes

a) less dense and falls ❑
b) more dense and rises ❑
c) less dense and rises ❑
d) more dense and falls ❑

5 Where is the warmest air in a room (1 mark)

a) next to the door ❑
b) as far away from the door as possible ❑
c) just above the floor ❑
d) just below the ceiling ❑

B

1 The incomplete diagrams to the right show how different sea breezes are created at the coast.

a) Draw on each of the diagrams arrows to show the directions of the convection currents created at different times of the day. (2 marks)

b) Explain how a convection current is set up during the day. (3 marks)

....

....

....

c) Explain how a convection current is set up during the night. (3 marks)

....

....

....

C

1 a) Explain why convection currents can transfer heat in liquids and gases but not through solids. (2 marks)

....

....

The diagram below shows a cavity wall.

b) Explain how heat can be transferred across the gap by convection. (3 marks)

....

....

....

....

....

....

c) What can be done to prevent this heat loss? Explain why this prevents heat loss. (3 marks)

....

....

....

....

....

2 The diagram below is of a domestic fridge.

a) Explain how the freezing compartment at the top of the fridge is able to cool the whole of the fridge. (3 marks)

....

....

....

....

....

....

....

3 The diagram to the right shows a spiral held above a small heat source.

Describe and explain what happens to the spiral. (3 marks)

....

....

....

....

....

How well did you do? 0-6 Try again 7-13 Getting there 14-21 Good work 22-27 Excellent!

Heat transfer – radiation

A

1 Heat travels to the Earth from the Sun by (1 mark)

a) convection ❑
b) radiation ❑
c) conduction ❑
d) evaporation ❑

2 When radiation strikes a dark rough surface it is likely to be (1 mark)

a) absorbed ❑
b) reflected ❑
c) refracted ❑
d) diffracted ❑

3 Good absorbers of heat are also (1 mark)

a) good convectors of heat ❑
b) good conductors of heat ❑
c) good insulators of heat ❑
d) good emitters of heat ❑

4 What kind of a surface should a teapot have if it is to reduce any heat loss by radiation? (1 mark)

a) matt ❑
b) black ❑
c) silvery ❑
d) metal ❑

5 To try to keep cool, people in hot countries could paint the outside of their houses (1 mark)

a) green ❑
b) black ❑
c) white ❑
d) brown ❑

B

1 Look carefully at the diagram to the right.

Shiny metal sheet
Dark metal sheet
Marble stuck to sheet by small piece of wax

a) How will most of the heat travel from the flame to the metal sheets?

.... (1 mark)

b) What happens to most of the heat that arrives at the shiny sheet?

.... (1 mark)

c) What happens to most of the heat that arrives at the dark coloured sheet? (1 mark)

....

d) Describe what happens to the marbles to confirm your answers for parts b and c. (2 marks)

....

2 The diagram to the right shows a solar heater used to heat water. Explain how the heater works. Include in your answer any important features which the reflector and the can have. (4 marks)

can containing water

....

....

C

1 Katy pours some very hot water into two containers that are the same size and made from the same material. One of the containers has a dark outer surface the second has a light shiny surface.

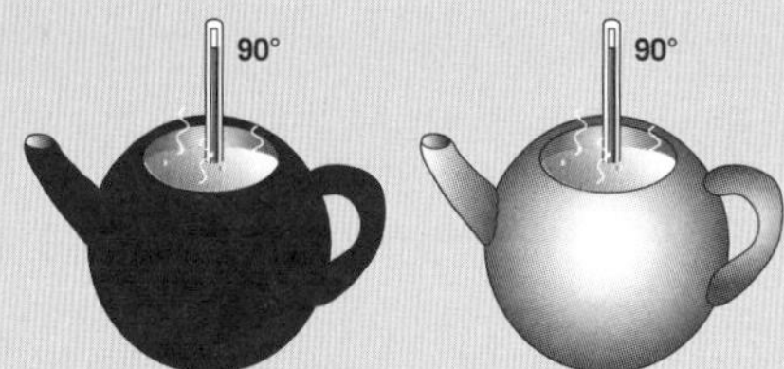

The temperature of the two lots of water is then measured every minute. The cooling curve for the water in the dark container is shown below.

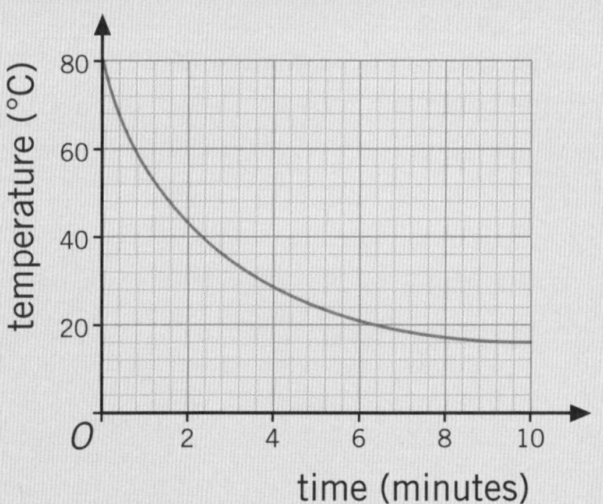

a) Sketch on the graph paper the cooling curve for the water in the silver container. (3 marks)

b) Explain briefly why the graph you have drawn has this shape. (2 marks)

....

....

....

....

....

c) What will be the final temperature of both of the waters? (1 mark)

....

2 The diagram below shows the construction of a thermos flask.

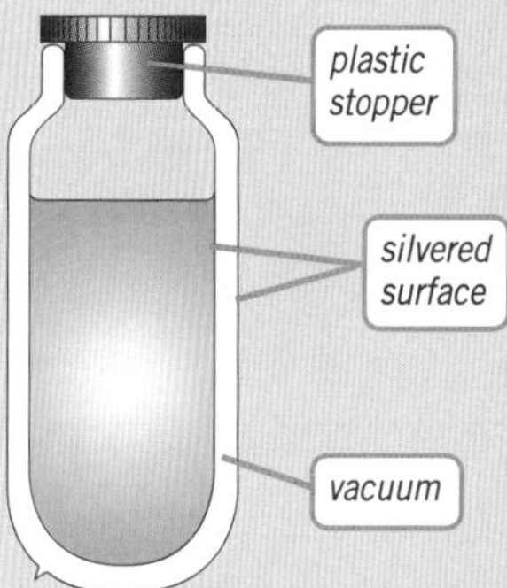

Describe how each of the following parts reduces heat loss from the flask.

a) plastic stopper (1 mark)

....

....

....

....

b) vacuum (1 mark)

....

....

....

....

c) silvered surfaces (1 mark)

....

....

....

....

How well did you do? ✗ 0-9 Try again 10-13 Getting there 14-18 Good work 19-23 Excellent!

Heat transfer – Warming, cooling, melting and boiling

A

1 Which of the following does not affect the size of the increase in temperature an object experiences when it is warmed? (1 mark)

a) its mass ❑
b) its temperature ❑
c) the material it is made from ❑
d) how much energy it is given ❑

2 Specific heat capacity is measured in (1 mark)

a) J/km/K
b) W/m^2
c) J/(kg K)
d) kWh

3 Which of the following is true? (1 mark)

a) There is no change in temperature whilst water boils. ❑
b) The melting point of water is 100°C. ❑
c) Heat is a measure of hotness. ❑
d) Temperature is a measure of energy. ❑

4 When steam condenses (1 mark)

a) it cools ❑
b) it expands ❑
c) it loses energy ❑
d) it loses mass ❑

5 The amount of energy needed to boil 1 kg of water at 100°C is called (1 mark)

a) the specific heat capacity of water ❑
b) the specific latent heat of fusion ❑
c) the specific heat of vaporisation ❑
d) the specific latent heat of vaporisation ❑

B

1 Calculate the missing values A–E in this table. (5 marks)

Substance	Specific heat capacity J/(kg K)	Change in temperature /°C	Mass of substance /kg	Energy lost or gained /kJ
water	4200	10	5	A
copper	380	B	10	76
iron	460	5	C	138
lead	140	200	100 g	D
X	E	50	2.5	50

2 Calculate the missing values A–C in this table. (3 marks)

Substance	Specific latent heat	Mass of substance /kg	Energy lost or gained /MJ
water	2.4 MJ/kg (vaporisation)	1.5	A
water	340 kJ/kg (fusion)	B	1.02
alcohol	C	10	1.8

C

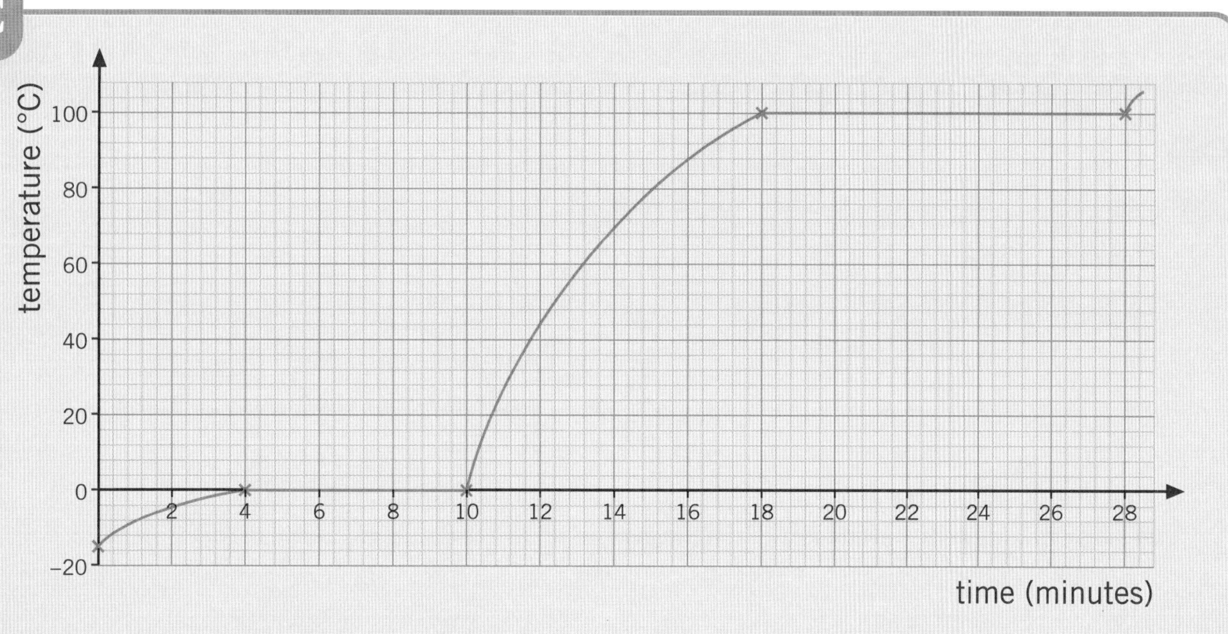

1 The graph above shows how the temperature of a block of ice changes when it is warmed.

a) What is the temperature of the ice before it is warmed? (1 mark)

....

b) At what temperature does the ice melt? (1 mark)

....

c) How long does the ice take to melt? (1 mark)

....

d) How long does the water take to boil? (1 mark)

....

e) Explain why the temperature of the water does not change as it is changing state. (2 marks)

....

....

....

....

f) Calculate the energy needed to melt 5 kg of ice without changing its temperature. The latent heat of fusion for ice is 340 kJ/kg. (3 marks)

....

....

....

....

....

....

g) Calculate the energy which will now have to be given to this water to raise its temperature to its boiling point. The specific heat capacity of water is 4 200 J/(kgK). (4 marks)

....

....

....

....

....

....

How well did you do? ✗ 0-10 Try again 11-15 Getting there 16-20 Good work 21-26 Excellent! ✓

Current, charge and resistance

A

1 Current in a wire is a flow of (1 mark)

a) protons ☐
b) ions ☐
c) electrons ☐
d) atoms ☐

2 If a charge of 20 C flows along a wire in 5 s the current flowing is (1 mark)

a) 100 A ☐
b) 15 A ☐
c) 0.25 A ☐
d) 4.0 A ☐

3 10 C of charge flow through a 12 V battery. How much energy does this charge receive? (1 mark)

a) 120 J ☐
b) 2 J ☐
c) 1.2 J ☐
d) 0.125 J ☐

4 A resistor which could be used to automatically control street lighting is called (1 mark)

a) an LDR ☐
b) a thermistor ☐
c) a thermostat ☐
d) a variable resistor ☐

5 A resistor which could be used to detect temperature changes is called (1 mark)

a) a diode ☐
b) a thermomstat ☐
c) a thermistor ☐
d) a filament bulb ☐

B

1 a) Calculate the potential difference across each of the resistors shown below.

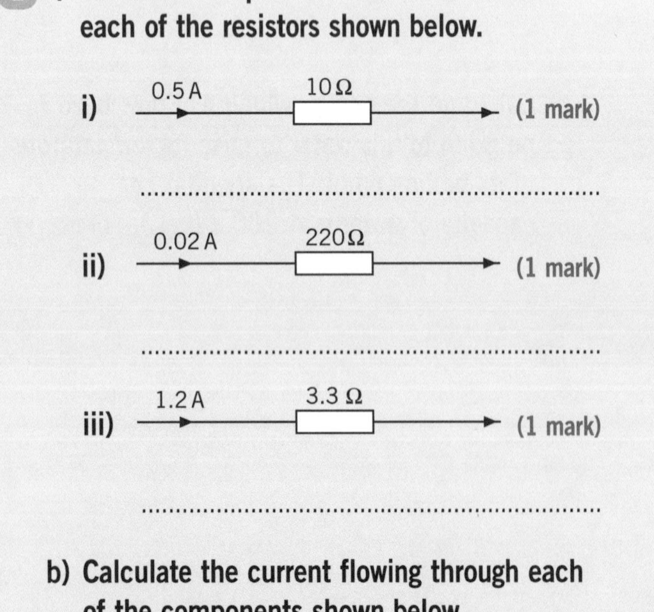

b) Calculate the current flowing through each of the components shown below.

i) 16 Ω, 4 V (1 mark)

....

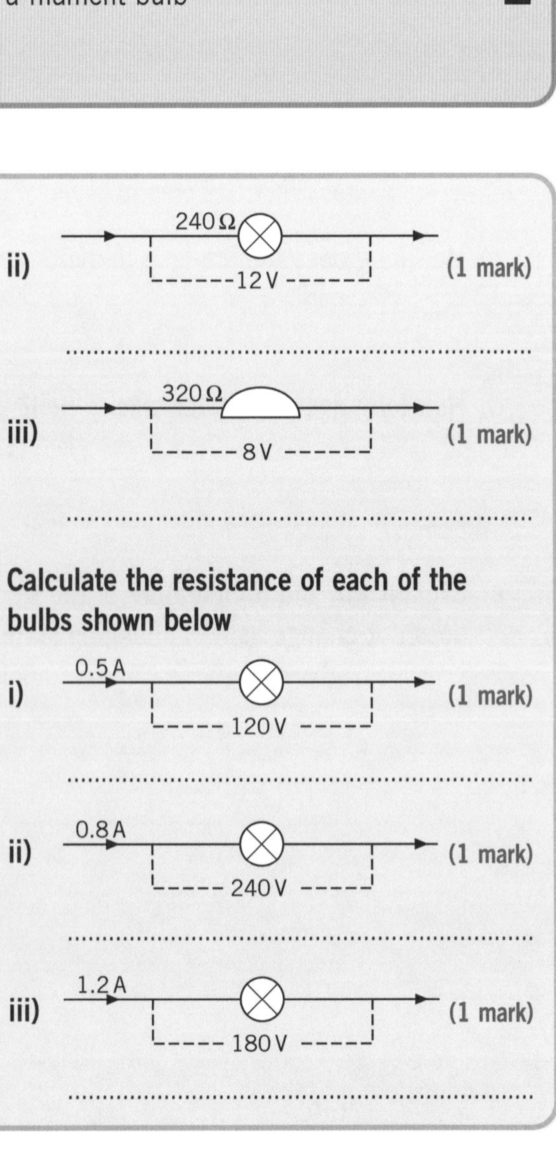

c) Calculate the resistance of each of the bulbs shown below

C

1 The diagram below shows a series circuit containing a battery, a switch, a bulb and a resistor.

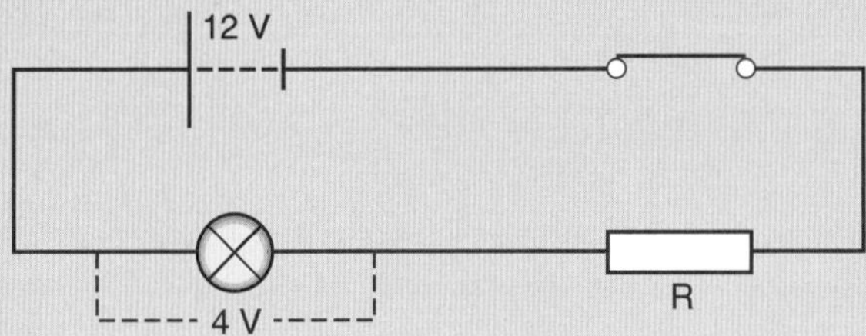

a) How much electrical energy is given to 3 C of charge that pass through the battery? (2 marks)

....

....

....

b) Describe the exact energy transfer that takes place when 1 C of charge passes through the bulb. (2 marks)

....

....

....

c) Describe the exact energy transfer that takes place when 2 C of charge pass through the resistor R. (3 marks)

....

....

....

....

....

2 Two pupils set up the circuit shown below to investigate the relationship between the potential difference applied across the ends of a piece of wire and the current that passes through it. Their results are shown in the table.

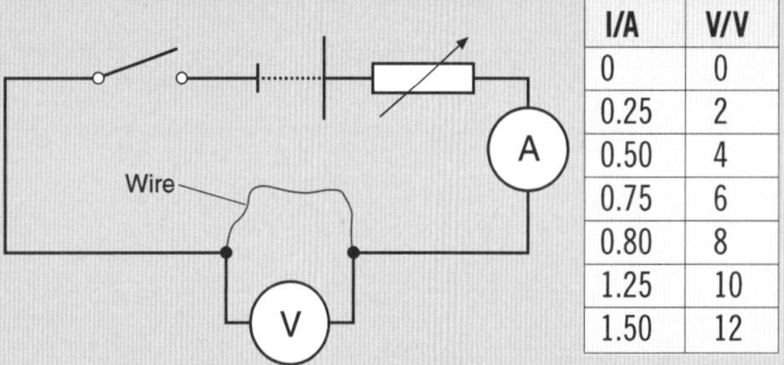

I/A	V/V
0	0
0.25	2
0.50	4
0.75	6
0.80	8
1.25	10
1.50	12

a) Using the results shown in the table plot a graph of current against potential difference. (6 marks)

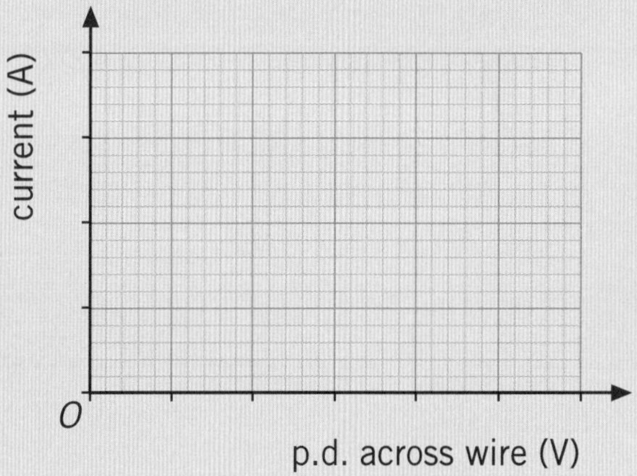

b) Draw in a line of best fit (1 mark)

....

c) Which pair of results did not fit the pattern? (1 mark)

....

d) Calculate the resistance of the wire. (2 marks)

....

How well did you do? ✗ 0-12 Try again 13-18 Getting there 19-24 Good work 25-31 Excellent! ✓

Electrical power

A

1 **How much electrical energy is changed into heat and light energy when a 100 W light bulb is turned on for 5 minutes?** (1 mark)

a) 300 J ☐
b) 30 kJ ☐
c) 500 J ☐
d) 3000 J ☐

2 **2 If an electric heater has a power rating of 3 kW it changes** (1 mark)

a) 3000 J of electrical energy into heat energy every hour ☐
b) 3 J of electrical energy into heat energy every second ☐
c) 3000 J of electrical energy into heat energy every second ☐
d) 3 kJ of electrical energy into heat energy every minute ☐

3 **Calculate the energy used in units when a 2 kW fire is turned on for 24 hours.** (1 mark)

a) 120 units ☐
b) 12 units ☐
c) 26 units ☐
d) 48 units ☐

4 **Calculate the cost of turning on a 2 kW tumble drier for 30 minutes, if the cost of one unit of electricity is 12.0p** (1 mark)

a) 6.0p ☐
b) 3.0p ☐
c) 12.0p ☐
d) 18.0p ☐

5 **The readings on an electricity meter at the beginning and end of a quarter show that a family has used 600 units of electrical energy. If the cost of 1 unit is 11.0 p and the standing charge is £12 calculate the total bill for this household (before VAT).** (1 mark)

a) £78 ☐
b) £72 ☐
c) £30 ☐
d) £60 ☐

B

1 **Fill in the missing words.** (9 marks)

Electrical appliances transfer .... into other .... of .... For example a television changes electrical energy into .... and .... The .... of an appliance is a measure of how .... the changes take place. This .... is measured in .... or kW.

2 **This bulb has a power rating of 60 W.**

60W

a) Explain what the above sentence tells you about the bulb (1 mark)

....

b) Calculate the amount of electrical energy that is converted into heat and light energy when a 60 W bulb is turned on for 1 min. (3 marks)

....

c) Calculate the amount of electrical energy that is converted into other forms when a hair dryer rated at 1200 W is used for 8 min. (3 marks)

....

C

ELECTRICITY BILL Charges for electricity used				
Present reading 80139	Previous reading 78579	Units used	Pence per unit 11.00	Charge amount
Quarterly standing charge Total				£ 12.00

1 The diagram above shows part of a domestic electricity bill.

a) How many units of electrical energy have been used by the household in this quarter? (1 mark)

b) What is the cost of this energy if 1 unit costs 11p? (1 mark)

c) What is the total bill for this household (before VAT) (1 mark)

d) How many units of electricity energy are used if a 100 W bulb is turned on for 1 day? (3 marks)

e) An electric motor converts 1.8 units of electrical energy into other forms of energy in 36 min. Calculate the power rating of the motor. (3 marks)

How well did you do? 0-12 Try again 13-18 Getting there 19-24 Good work 25-30 Excellent!

Motors and generators

A

1 Which of the following will not make a motor turn more quickly? (1 mark)

a) increase the number of turns on the coil ❑
b) increase the current ❑
c) increase the strength of the magnet ❑
d) replace the split ring with two full rings ❑

2 Which of the following statements is true for a current carrying wire placed between the poles of a magnet? (1 mark)

a) The wire will move from a strong part of the magnetic field to a weaker part. ❑
b) The wire may move from the north pole of the magnet to the south pole. ❑
c) The wire may move from the south pole of the magnet to the north pole. ❑
d) The wire will be pushed into the strongest part of the field between the poles of the magnet. ❑

3 Which of the following will produce an induced voltage across a wire? (1 mark)

a) holding the wire stationary between the poles of a magnet ❑
b) moving the wire from the north pole of a magnet to the south pole ❑
c) moving the wire across magnetic field lines ❑
d) moving the wire from the south pole of a magnet to the north ❑

4 Which of the following statements is untrue for an alternator? (1 mark)

a) an alternator produces direct current ❑
b) an alternator produces alternating current ❑
c) an alternator produces current which is continually changing direction ❑
d) an alternator produces induced currents ❑

5 Which of the following will not increase the current produced by a generator? (1 mark)

a) using a coil with more turns ❑
b) using a stronger magnet ❑
c) turning the coil more quickly ❑
d) using thicker brushes ❑

B

1 The diagram shows a magnet being pushed into a long coil. As the magnet moves into the coil the needle of the meter is seen to move a little to the right.

Describe what would happen if

a) The magnet is withdrawn from the coil quickly .... (2 marks)

b) The south pole of the magnet is pushed into the coil slowly .... (2 marks)

c) The magnet is held stationary in side the coil .... (1 mark)

d) The magnet is held stationary but the coil is moved to the right .... (1 mark)

2 Fill in the gaps to give a full explanation of how a simple bicycle dynamo works. (9 marks)

The cyclist pedals and his .... rotate. Leaning against one of these is a .... As this turns a .... inside the dynamo .... around. Its .... cuts through a .... A .... is induced in the .... This is used to make the .... glow.

C

1 A loop of wire is placed between the poles of a magnet.

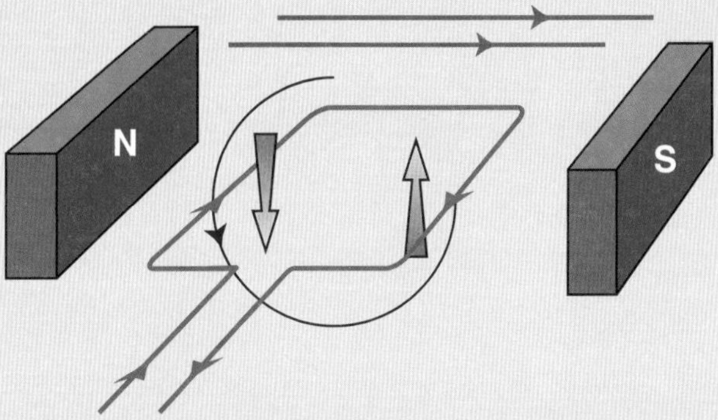

a) Explain why the loop begins to rotate when current flows through it. (3 marks)

b) Why does the loop stop rotating when it is vertical? (2 marks)

c) Explain how the use of a split ring (commutator) enables the coil to rotate continuously. (3 marks)

2 a) What is alternating current? (1 mark)

The diagram below shows a simple alternator

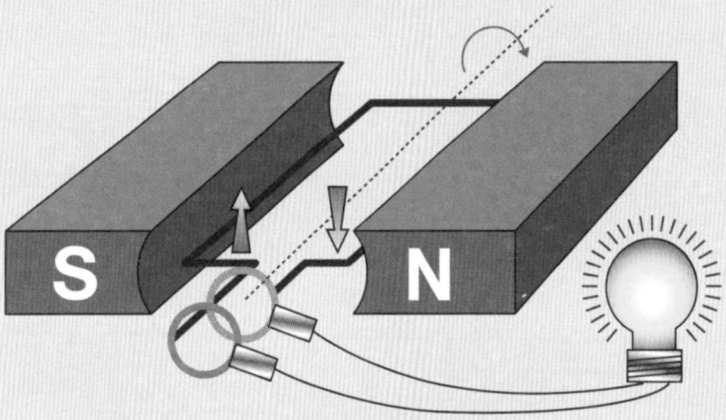

b) Explain why the alternator produces alternating current. (2 marks)

c) State three ways in which the current being produced by the alternator could be increased. (3 marks)

How well did you do? ✗ 0-13 Try again 14-20 Getting there 21-27 Good work 28-34 Excellent! ✓

Domestic electricity

A

1 **The earth wire in a three-pin plug is** (1 mark)

a) green ☐
b) yellow ☐
c) brown ☐
d) green and yellow ☐

2 **A current which is continuously changing direction is called** (1 mark)

a) an alternating current ☐
b) an alternator current ☐
c) a direct current ☐
d) an induced current ☐

3 **The wire through which electrical energy travels to an appliance is known as** (1 mark)

a) the earth wire ☐
b) the live wire ☐
c) the connecting wire ☐
d) the neutral wire ☐

4 **Which of the following is not a common fuse in the UK?** (1 mark)

a) 1 A ☐
b) 3 A ☐
c) 10 A ☐
d) 13 A ☐

5 **The voltage from the mains in the UK is approximately** (1 mark)

a) 200 V ☐
b) 240 V ☐
c) 110 V ☐
d) 12 V ☐

B

1 **The diagram to the right shows the inside of a three-pin plug.**

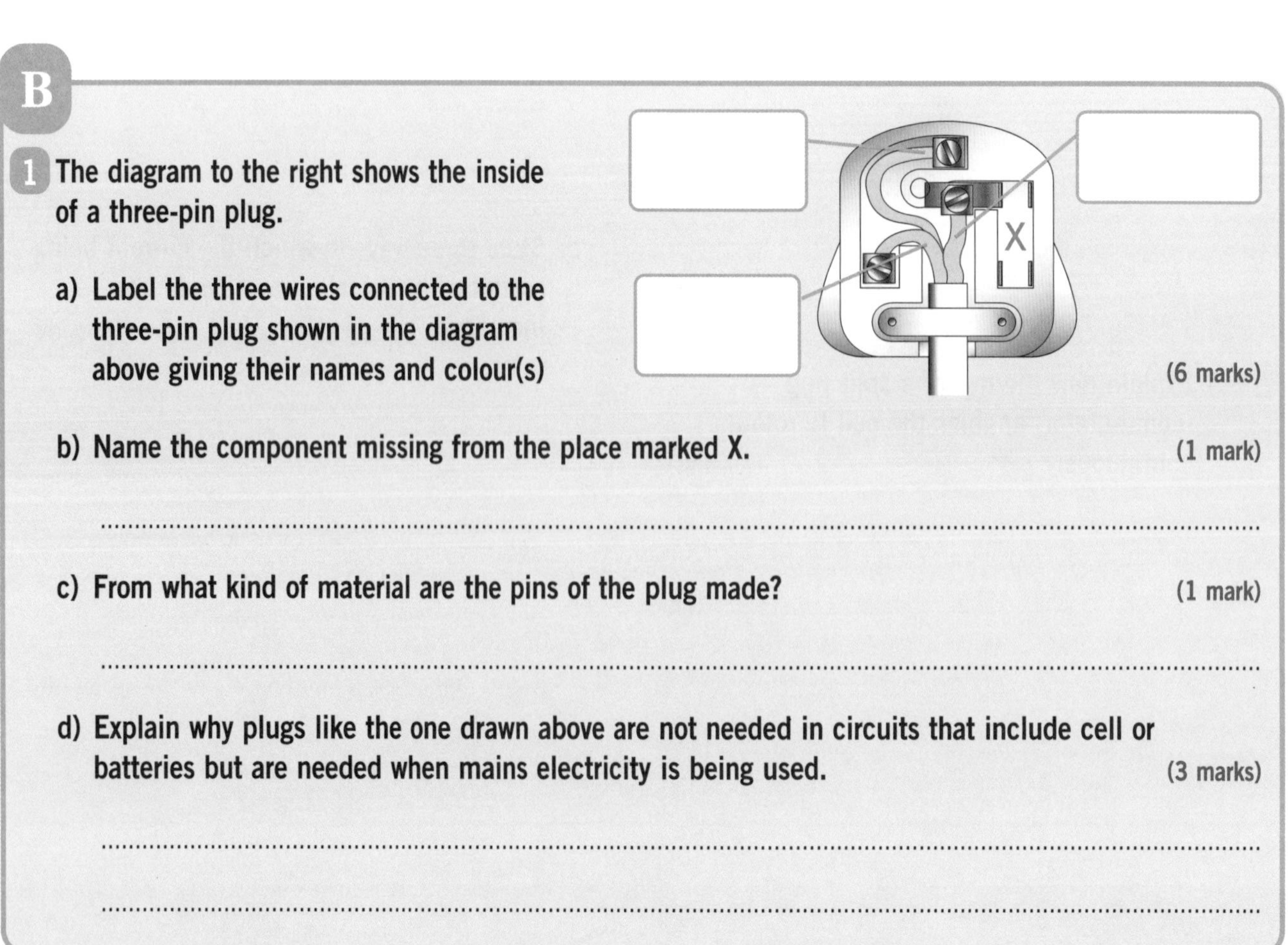

a) **Label the three wires connected to the three-pin plug shown in the diagram above giving their names and colour(s)** (6 marks)

b) **Name the component missing from the place marked X.** (1 mark)

....

c) **From what kind of material are the pins of the plug made?** (1 mark)

....

d) **Explain why plugs like the one drawn above are not needed in circuits that include cell or batteries but are needed when mains electricity is being used.** (3 marks)

....

....

C

To gain full marks you must show all your workings for numerical questions and include the correct units in your answers.

1 The diagrams below show two types of kettle. Kettle A has a metal outer casing and kettle B has a plastic outer casing.

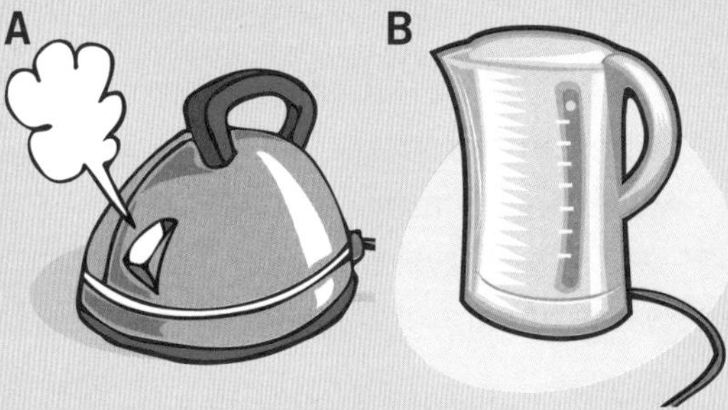

a) Explain why someone using kettle A might receive a shock if the heating element is faulty and there is no earth wire connected. (2 marks)

....

....

....

....

b) Explain why there is no need for an earth wire to be connected to kettle B. (2 marks)

....

....

....

....

....

c) What is the name of the kind of insulation provided by the plastic casing of kettle B? (1 mark)

....

2 The diagram below shows a 13 A cartridge fuse.

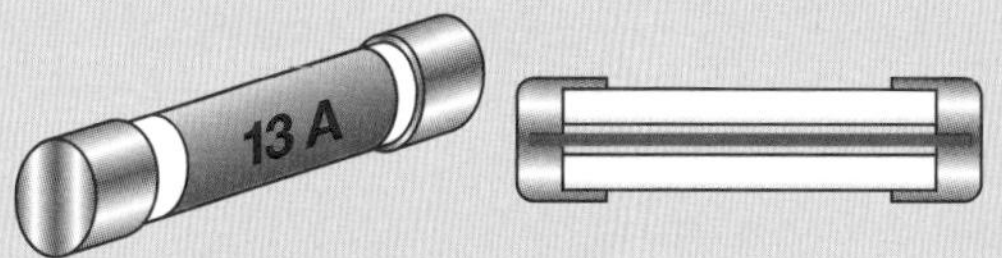

a) Explain how this fuse works and why we should include a fuse similar to that shown above in all mains circuits. (4 marks)

....

....

....

....

....

....

....

....

b) You are given fuses that have a rating of 1 A, 3 A and 13 A. Assuming that the mains supply voltage is 240 V calculate the correct fuse needed for

i) a 600 W electric iron (3 marks)

....

....

....

ii) a 2 kW electric heater (3 marks)

....

....

....

How well did you do? ✗ 0-12 Try again 13-18 Getting there 19-24 Good work 25-31 Excellent! ✓

Waves

A

1 Which of the following is not a transverse wave? (1 mark)

a) sound waves ☐
b) X-rays ☐
c) radio waves ☐
d) microwaves ☐

2 The frequency of a wave is (1 mark)

a) the height of the wave ☐
b) the distance between the peak of one wave and the peak of the next ☐
c) the number of waves made by the source each second ☐
d) the distance between a peak and a trough ☐

3 Which of these is not a property of all waves? (1 mark)

a) radioactivity ☐
b) reflection ☐
c) refraction ☐
d) diffraction ☐

4 Which of the following information about P- waves is untrue? (1 mark)

a) P-waves are transverse waves ☐
b) P-waves travel faster than S-waves ☐
c) P-waves can travel through liquids ☐
d) P-waves can travel through solids ☐

5 Which of the following information about S- waves is untrue? (1 mark)

a) S-waves can travel through liquids ☐
b) S-waves are transverse waves ☐
c) S- waves can travel through solids ☐
d) S-waves travel more slowly than P-waves ☐

B

1 Calculate the values A–F using the information in the table below. (6 marks)

Wave velocity	Wave frequency	Wavelength
A	85 Hz	4 m
20 m/s	5 Hz	B
330 m/s	C	1.5 m
D	200 kHz	1500 m
50 m/s	E	0.2 m
340 m/s	20 kHz	F

2 Name three differences between P-waves and S-waves. (3 marks)

a) ....

b) ....

c) ....

C

1 a) Name one source of seismic waves. (1mark)

....

....

b) Explain how a building on the surface of the Earth will move if a P-wave passes through its foundations. (1mark)

....

....

....

....

c) Explain how a building on the surface of the Earth will move if an S-wave passes through its foundations. (1mark)

....

....

....

....

2 The diagram below shows P-waves and S-waves passing through the Earth

a) Why are there no S-waves in the region marked X? (2 marks)

....

....

....

....

....

....

b) Why do both types of wave gradually change direction as they travel through the Earth? (2 marks)

....

....

....

....

....

....

....

c) Why do both types of waves sometimes change direction suddenly? (1 mark)

....

....

....

....

How well did you do? ✗ 0-8 Try again 9-13 Getting there 14-17 Good work 18-22 Excellent! ✓

The electromagnetic spectrum

A

1 **Which of the following types of waves is used for cooking?** (1 mark)

a) gamma rays ❑
b) X-rays ❑
c) ultraviolet waves ❑
d) microwaves ❑

2 **Which of the following waves has the longest wavelength?**

a) radio waves ❑
b) visible light ❑
c) infrared waves ❑
d) microwaves ❑

3 **Which group of waves in the electromagnetic spectrum has the greatest penetrating power?** (1 mark)

a) ultraviolet waves ❑
b) X-rays ❑
c) microwaves ❑
d) radio waves ❑

4 **Which of the following is not a use of infrared waves?** (1 mark)

a) sun lamps ❑
b) remote controls for TV ❑
c) night vision cameras ❑
d) heating lamps ❑

5 **Which of the following is not a use of ultraviolet waves?** (1 mark)

a) sun lamps ❑
b) detecting forged bank notes ❑
c) night vision cameras ❑
d) checking for security markings ❑

B

1 **a) Unscramble the letters to reveal seven parts of the electromagnetic spectrum.** (7 marks)

vsrdweoaai ....
rvmcweaios ....
lraioelttvu ....
eaindfrr ....
axsyr ....
smmaaaygr ....
gveiiistbllh ....

b) Fill in the missing words. (14 marks)

X-rays have a very short .... and a very high .... They are very penetrating and so are often used in .... to look inside .... Over exposure to these waves can cause .... So people who work with them everyday must take .... such as standing behind a .... or wearing a ....

Ultraviolet waves are emitted by the .... They cause our skin to .... Over exposure can cause .... To avoid this we can use a cream called a .... Ultraviolet rays make some chemicals .... or ....

C

1 The diagram above shows the electromagnetic spectrum.

radio waves, microwaves, infrared, ultru violet, gamma rays

A B

a) What are the names of the two groups of waves A and B? (2 marks)

....

....

b) What property of a wave increases as we move from left to right in the electromagnetic spectrum shown above? (1 mark)

....

....

c) What property of a wave decreases as we move from left to right in the electromagnetic spectrum shown above? (1 mark)

....

....

d) Name three properties that all these waves possess. (3 marks)

....

....

....

....

....

....

2 a) Name three possible consequences of ultraviolet light being absorbed by the skin. (3 marks)

....

....

....

....

....

....

b) Suggest two ways in which we can avoid the problems created by excessive exposure to ultraviolet light. (2 marks)

....

....

....

....

....

c) Explain in your own words why microwave ovens cook foods much more quickly than conventional ovens. (3 marks)

....

....

....

....

....

....

....

How well did you do? ✗ 0-16 **Try again** 17-24 **Getting there** 25-32 **Good work** 33-41 **Excellent!** ✓

Analogue and digital signals

A

1 When a ray enters or leaves a glass block it may change direction. This is called (1 mark)

a) reflection ❑
b) refraction ❑
c) diffraction ❑
d) interference ❑

2 When a ray emerging from glass strikes the boundary at an angle greater than the critical angle it will be (1 mark)

a) totally internally refracted ❑
b) totally internally diffracted ❑
c) totally internally reflected ❑
d) totally internally dispersed ❑

3 Which of the following is not an advantage of replacing copper wires with optical fibres? (1 mark)

a) optical fibres are cheaper ❑
b) messages in optical fibres are more secure ❑
c) optical fibres can carry more messages ❑
d) optical fibres are transparent ❑

4 Analogue signals vary (1 mark)

a) in a discontinuous manner ❑
b) with distance ❑
c) in a continuous manner ❑
d) between the values of 0 and 1 ❑

5 Digital signals (1 mark)

a) have only two values 1 or 2 ❑
b) can be processed by computers ❑
c) are continuous signals ❑
d) are louder than analogue signals ❑

B

1 Draw a labelled diagram in the space to the right to show how a signal travels down an optical fibre. (4 marks)

2 Which of these sentences are true and which are false? (10 marks)

	true	false
a) When a ray of light enters a glass block it slows down	❑	❑
b) When a ray of light leaving glass strikes the boundary at an angle less than the critical angle total internal reflection takes place.	❑	❑
c) Copper wires are replacing optical fibres in modern telecommunication systems.	❑	❑
d) Optical fibres can carry more signals than copper wires.	❑	❑
e) Analogue radio waves gain energy as they travel to the receiver.	❑	❑
f) Digital radio waves lose energy as they travel to the receiver.	❑	❑
g) Repeater stations amplify signals making them weaker.	❑	❑
h) Digital signals need to be converted back to analogue signals before they can be processed by computers.	❑	❑
i) Digital signals arrive at the receiver with fewer distortions.	❑	❑
j) Visible light can be used to send signals along optical fibres.	❑	❑

C

1 The diagram below shows an analogue signal i) as it is transmitted, ii) after it has travelled to the first repeater station and iii) after it has been amplified.

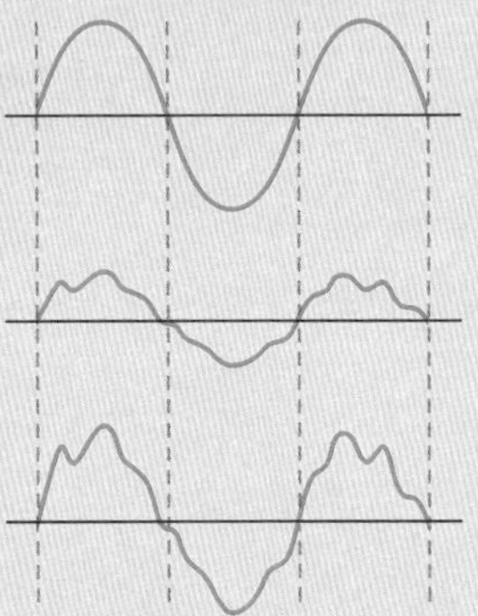

a) Explain why signals need to be amplified at repeater stations. (1 mark)

....

....

....

b) What is noise and what effect does it have on an analogue signal? (2 marks)

....

....

....

....

c) What happens to noise at the repeater station and what effect does this have on the final received signal? (2 marks)

....

....

....

....

d) In the spaces below draw 3 diagrams showing

i) a transmitted digital signal (1 mark)

ii) the digital signal as it arrives at a repeater station (1 mark)

iii) the digital signal as it leaves the repeater station (1 mark)

e) Give one advantage of sending a message as a digital signal rather than an analogue signal. (1 mark)

....

....

....

How well did you do? ✗ 0-11 Try again 12-16 Getting there 17-22 Good work 23-28 Excellent! ✓

Nuclear radiation

A

1 Alpha particles (1 mark)

a) are poor ionisers ❑
b) are unaffected by electric fields ❑
c) consist of 2 protons and 2 neutrons ❑
d) are uncharged ❑

2 Beta particles (1 mark)

a) are fast moving electrons ❑
b) are more penetrating than gamma rays ❑
c) are uncharged ❑
d) are unaffected by magnetic fields ❑

3 Gamma rays (1 mark)

a) are not very penetrating ❑
b) are deflected by magnetic fields ❑
c) are deflected by electric fields ❑
d) travel at the speed of light ❑

4 Most of our background radiation comes from (1 mark)

a) medical sources ❑
b) space ❑
c) naturally occurring materials in the ground ❑
d) nuclear weapons ❑

5 Which of the following statements is untrue (1 mark)

a) A dosimeter monitors exposure to radiation. ❑
b) Alpha radiation is the least penetrating radiation and therefore likely to damage living cells. ❑
c) Thick sheets of a dense metal are needed to stop gamma radiation. ❑
d) A radioactive substance gives out radiation. ❑

B

1 The list below shows several different sources of radioactivity. Show as a pie chart the contribution each of these sources makes to the background radiation. (5 marks)

rocks and soil 65% medical sources 12%
air and food 12% outside the Earth (space) 10%
fall-out and leaks from nuclear installations 1%

2 Which of the following statements are true and which are false? (8 marks)

	true	false
a) Alpha particles are slow moving, high penetrating helium nuclei.	❑	❑
b) Gamma waves move at the speed of light.	❑	❑
c) Beta particles are deviated a lot by magnetic and electric fields because they don't move very quickly.	❑	❑
d) Alpha particles are not deviated a lot by magnetic and electric fields because they are moving very quickly.	❑	❑
e) Gamma radiation is very penetrating and therefore produces lots of ions as it passes through objects.	❑	❑
f) Gamma radiation is uncharged and therefore not affected by magnetic or electric fields.	❑	❑
g) Alpha radiation is very similar to X-rays.	❑	❑
h) Beta particles are more penetrating than alpha particles because they are smaller.	❑	❑

C

1 a) Name one illness that may be caused by exposure to radiation. (1 mark)

b) Explain why alpha radiation is likely to cause less damage to living tissue than the other two types of radiation if the source of the radiation is outside the body. (2 marks)

c) Explain why alpha radiation is likely to cause more damage to living tissue than the other types of radiation if the source of the radiation is inside the body. (2 marks)

d) What is a dosimeter and what does it do? (1 mark)

e) Give one example of the kind of person who might need a dosimeter. (1 mark)

2 You are given two radioactive sources. Both sources emit two types of radiation. It is thought that one of the sources is emitting alpha and gamma radiation and the other beta and gamma radiation.

Describe an experiment you would carry out to discover which types of radiation each source was emitting. (You can assume that there is no background radiation) (5 marks)

How well did you do? ✗ 0-12 Try again 13-18 Getting there 19-24 Good work 25-30 Excellent! ✓

Uses of radioactivity

A

1 What is produced by the alpha emitter inside a smoke detector? (1 mark)

a) atoms ❑
b) ions ❑
c) protons ❑
d) neutrons ❑

2 In which of these situations would a radioactive tracer not be used? (1 mark)

a) sterilisation of food ❑
b) to monitor the flow of blood in the body ❑
c) to check for leaks in a gas pipe ❑
d) to check the progress of food through the digestive system ❑

3 Which of the following combinations could be used to monitor the thickness of a material produced as a sheet? (1 mark)

a) gamma radiation to monitor the thickness of paper ❑
b) alpha radiation to monitor the thickness of card ❑
c) beta radiation to monitor the thickness of paper ❑
d) alpha radiation to monitor the thickness of steel ❑

4 A narrow beam of radiation can be used to kill cancerous cells. This treatment is called (1 mark)

a) radiotherapy ❑
b) radioactivity ❑
c) sterilisation ❑
d) radioscopy ❑

5 Which of the following might be exposed to gamma radiation in order to kill bacteria? (1 mark)

a) antiseptic ❑
b) surgeons' hands ❑
c) disinfectant ❑
d) surgical instruments ❑

B

1 The diagram to the right shows a smoke detector. A description of how it works is given below but parts of it have been omitted. Fill in the missing words. (9 marks)

The smoke detector contains a radioisotope which emits .... These collide with .... creating .... As a result a .... flows. If .... enters the detector fewer .... are produced so the .... and the alarm ....

2 a) What causes food to rot?.. (1 mark)

b) How in the home can we slow down the rate at which a food rots? (1 mark)

....

c) Explain how radioactivity can be used so that foods keep for much longer. (2 marks)

....

C

1 The diagram below shows how a radioactive source is used in radiotherapy.

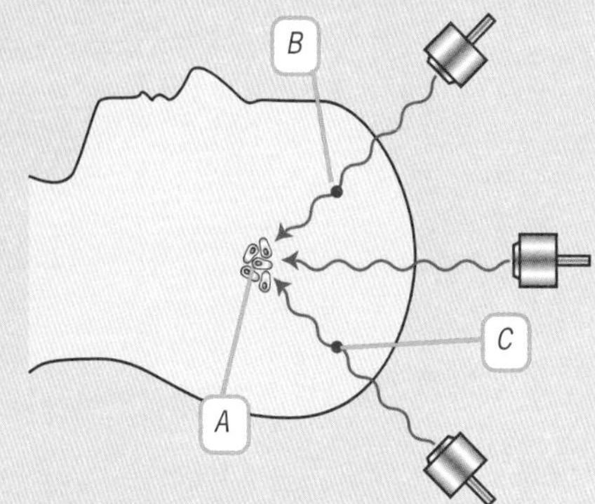

a) Name the type of radioactivity emitted by the source. (1 mark)

....

....

....

b) What happens to the cancerous cells at A? (2 marks)

....

....

....

c) Why does this not happen to cells at B or C? (1 mark)

....

....

....

....

....

2 The diagram below shows a man using a radiation detector. The fluid in the pipe has been labelled with a gamma emitter.

a) Suggest one material which might be flowing through the pipe. (1 mark)

....

b) What is the man trying to find? (1 mark)

....

c) How will he know when he finds it? (1 mark)

....

....

d) Why is the fluid not labelled with an alpha or beta emitter? (1 mark)

....

....

....

e) Give one advantage of this technique. (2 marks)

....

....

....

How well did you do? ✗ 0-11 Try again 12-17 Getting there 18-23 Good work 24-29 Excellent! ✓

The Earth in space

A

1 Which of the following statements about comets is not true? (1 mark)

a) They travel fastest when furthest from the Sun. ❑
b) They are made of rock-like pieces of ice. ❑
c) A comet's tail is produced by ice that has melted. ❑
d) They have very elliptical orbits. ❑

2 We can see stars and moons because (1 mark)

a) they reflect light ❑
b) they are luminous ❑
c) stars emit light and the moons reflect light ❑
d) they are non-luminous ❑

3 Which of the following is not a use for an artificial satellite? (1 mark)

a) measuring the strength of earthquakes ❑
b) monitoring weather conditions on the Earth ❑
c) communications ❑
d) exploring deep space ❑

4 The planets are held in orbit around the Sun by (1 mark)

a) gravitational forces ❑
b) electrostatic forces ❑
c) magnetic forces ❑
d) astronomical forces ❑

5 Name one natural satellite (1 mark)

a) an asteroid ❑
b) the Earth ❑
c) Mars ❑
d) the Moon ❑

B

1 There are 14 words or phrases connected to this topic hidden in this word search. Can you find them all? (14 marks)

S	A	T	U	R	N	M	J	A	L	N
A	O	C	Q	C	U	B	V	Q	R	Z
T	P	L	U	T	O	R	I	H	U	P
E	S	T	A	R	J	M	A	N	W	A
L	D	M	A	R	S	I	E	N	S	N
L	R	O	Q	U	S	K	H	T	U	S
I	F	O	V	G	L	Y	E	S	D	S
T	S	N	K	T	C	R	S	G	T	O
E	A	R	T	H	O	B	A	T	X	F
O	J	U	P	I	T	E	R	Y	E	E
M	E	P	D	W	O	R	B	I	T	M

2 a) What is an NEO?.. (1 mark)

b) Why might an NEO be dangerous to us?.. (1 mark)

c) What are some scientists suggesting we should do about the problem of NEOs? (2 marks)

....

....

C

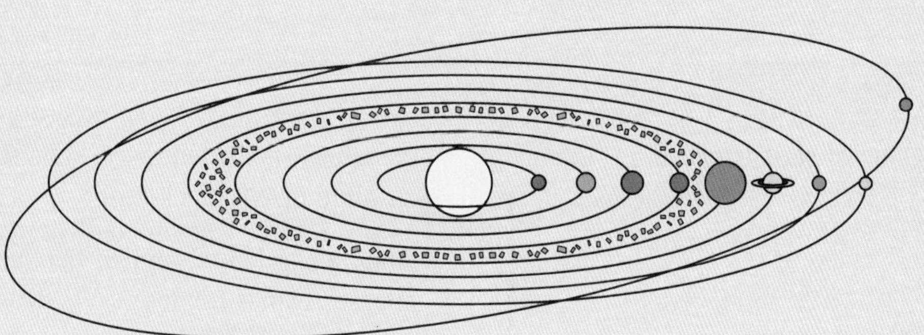

1 The diagram above shows part of our solar system.

a) What is a comet? (2 marks)

....

....

b) What is an asteroid? (2 marks)

....

....

c) Explain how scientists think asteroids were first formed? (2 marks)

....

....

d) How does the orbit of a comet differ from the orbit of a planet? (1 mark)

....

....

e) What kinds of forces keep objects in orbit around the Sun? (1 mark)

....

....

f) On the diagram above draw in the orbit of a comet. (1 mark)

g) Where in the orbit of a comet is it travelling fastest? (1 mark)

....

....

....

h) What is a satellite? (1 mark)

....

....

....

i) Explain the difference between a natural satellite and an artificial satellite. Give examples of each in your explanation. (3 marks)

....

....

....

....

....

....

How well did you do? ✗ 1-14 Try again 15-22 Getting there 23-29 Good work 30-37 Excellent! ✓

Stars and the universe

A

1 A very large group of stars is called a (1 mark)

a) constellation ☐
b) galaxy ☐
c) milky way ☐
d) solar system ☐

2 Which of these statements is not true? (1 mark)

a) Distant galaxies are moving away from us at very high speeds. ☐
b) Distant galaxies emit light with red shift. ☐
c) All distant galaxies are much smaller than closer galaxies. ☐
d) Most galaxies are moving away from us. ☐

3 Which of the following is the correct sequence for the life of a star? (1 mark)

a) nebula, red giant, main sequence, white dwarf, black dwarf ☐
b) main sequence, nebula, red giant, white dwarf, black dwarf ☐
c) nebula, red giant, main sequence, black dwarf, white dwarf ☐
d) nebula, main sequence, red giant, white dwarf, black dwarf ☐

4 When a star is first formed the energy it releases comes from (1 mark)

a) nuclear fusion between nuclei of hydrogen ☐
b) nuclear fission between nuclei of hydrogen ☐
c) chemical reactions between hydrogen and helium ☐
d) the high pressures created by the extremely large gravitational forces present ☐

5 The presence of background microwaves in all parts of the universe is evidence for (1 mark)

a) the presence of Black Holes ☐
b) the Big Bang Theory of the universe ☐
c) the Big Crunch Theory of the universe ☐
d) the birth of stars from interstellar dust ☐

B

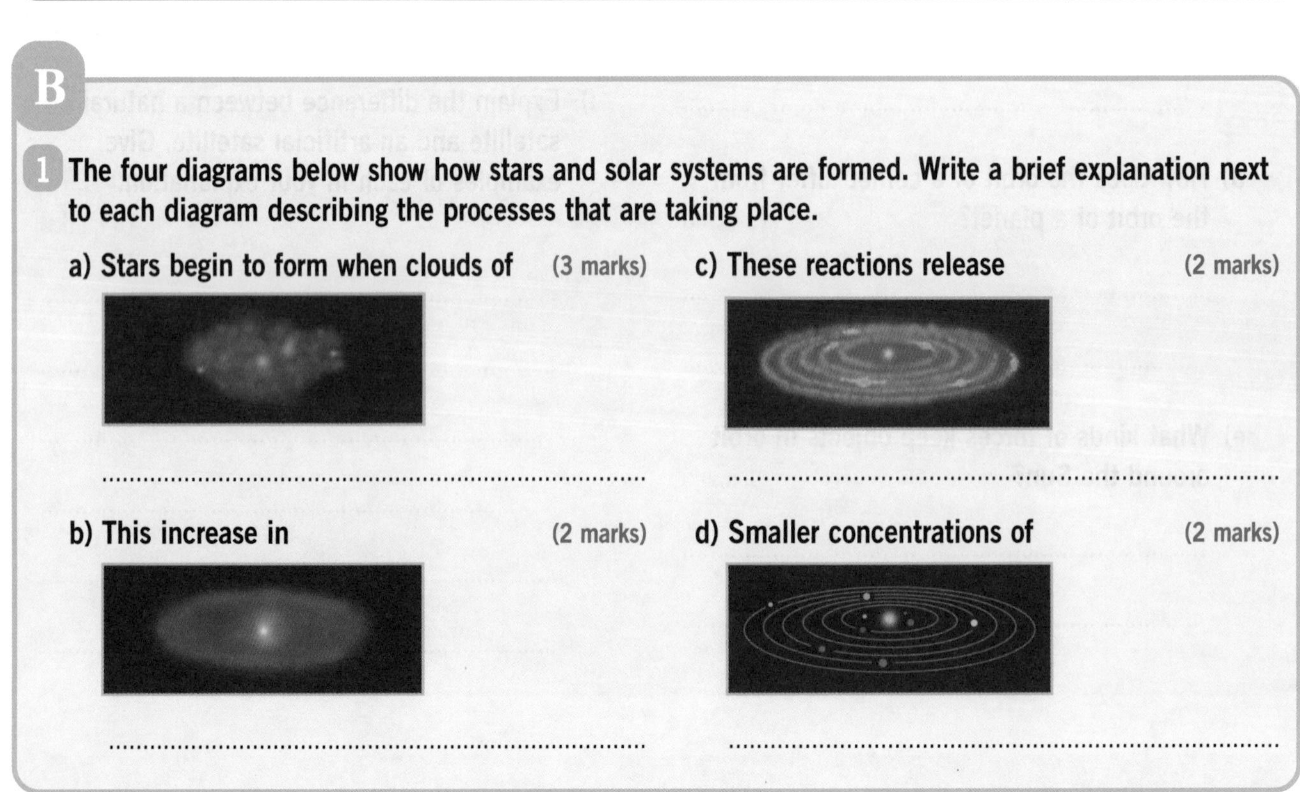

1 The four diagrams below show how stars and solar systems are formed. Write a brief explanation next to each diagram describing the processes that are taking place.

a) Stars begin to form when clouds of (3 marks)

....

b) This increase in (2 marks)

....

c) These reactions release (2 marks)

....

d) Smaller concentrations of (2 marks)

....

C

1 Stars gradually change with time.

a) What forces pull matter together when a star first forms? (1 mark)

....

....

b) What kinds of reactions begin as the matter is pulled together? (1 mark)

....

....

c) What is released by these reactions? (1 mark)

....

....

d) How do we describe a star after it has been formed and the forces of expansion and the forces of attraction are balanced? (1 mark)

....

....

....

e) What is a supernova? (1 mark)

....

....

....

f) What remains at the end of the life of a star which has 'gone supernova'? (1 mark)

....

....

2 a) What is the Big Bang Theory? (2 marks)

....

....

....

....

....

....

b) What proof do scientists have that supports the Big Bang Theory? (2 marks)

....

....

....

....

....

....

c) Suggest two possible futures for the Universe. (2 marks)

....

....

....

....

....

....

How well did you do? ✗ 0-10 Try again 11-15 Getting there 16-20 Good work 21-26 Excellent! ✓

Exploring space

A

1 What is a flyby? (1 mark)

a) a kind of aircraft ❑
b) a kind of probe ❑
c) a kind of telescope ❑
d) an asteroid ❑

2 Which of the following is unlikely to be analysed using a lander? (1 mark)

a) soil samples ❑
b) magnetic field strength ❑
c) chemical content of atmosphere ❑
d) speed of light in a vacuum ❑

3 Large optical telescopes are often built on mountain tops because (1 mark)

a) it is then closer to the stars and planets ❑
b) it is quieter ❑
c) there is less light pollution ❑
d) there are no vibrations from passing traffic ❑

4 Which of the following is not a benefit of exploring space? (1 mark)

a) smoke detectors ❑
b) non-stick frying pans ❑
c) unleaded petrol ❑
d) ultrasound scanners ❑

5 Which of the following is the name of a telescope which is orbiting the Earth? (1 mark)

a) Big Brother ❑
b) Sky satellite ❑
c) Bubble telescope ❑
d) Hubble telescope ❑

B

1 The table below contains data about the planets in our solar system.

Planet	Distance from Sun compared with the Earth	Diameter compared with the Earth	Mass compared with the Earth	Day length	Year length	Average surface temperature in °C
Mercury	0.4	0.4	0.05	60	0.2	120
Venus	0.7	0.9	0.8	240	0.6	460
Earth	1	1	1	1	1	15
Mars	1.5	0.5	0.1	2	2	–25
Jupiter	5	11	320	0.4	12	–73
Saturn	10	10	95	0.4	30	–140
Uranus	19	4	15	0.7	84	–200
Neptune	30	3.5	17	0.7	160	–200
Pluto	40	0.2	0.003	6	250	–220

a) What is the length of one day on the most massive planet in our solar system? (1 mark)
b) What is the length of one year on the planet most distant from the Sun? (1 mark)
c) How long does it take for the planet Uranus to rotate three times around its axis? (1 mark)
d) Which planet takes the smallest time to make one complete orbit of the Sun? (1 mark)
e) Which planet is the second most massive? (1 mark)
f) Which planet is six times further from the Sun than Jupiter? (1 mark)
g) Which planet apart from the Earth has a surface temperature which suggests that there could be life there? (1 mark)

C

1 Probes are used to explore our solar system.

The photo below shows the probe Mars Observer which was sent to Mars in 1992.

a) Explain the difference between a flyby probe and a lander. (2 marks)

....

....

....

....

b) What kind of information might be gathered by a flyby probe? (1 mark)

....

....

....

c) What kind of information might be gathered by a lander? (1 mark)

....

....

....

d) Why is most of the exploration of our solar system carried out by unmanned spacecraft and not manned spacecraft? (1 mark)

....

....

....

....

e) Describe some of the problems that might be experienced by astronauts who have to live in zero gravity for more than just a few days. (2 marks)

....

....

....

....

....

f) Describe one way in which the problems you have described in part e can be overcome. (1 mark)

....

....

....

g) Describe two more extra considerations that have to be given to a spacecraft when planning a manned flight. (2 marks)

....

....

....

....

How well did you do? ✗ 0-8 Try again 9-13 Getting there 14-17 Good work 18-22 Excellent! ✓

Notes

Notes